Field Studies 7 (1990), 531–593

BRITISH SAWFLIES (Hymenoptera: S
A key to adults of the gen

ADAM W.

Senior Keeper, Natural History, Herber

ABSTRA

Dichotomous keys to adults of the 109 gener ing in Britain are provided. Brief sections on life history, ecol, collecting and morphology are included. Recent taxonomic changes have been incorporated.

CONTENTS

INTRODUCTION

Sawflies are considered to be the most primitive members of the insect order Hymenoptera, which includes the bees, ants and wasps. The sawflies form a complete sub-order, the Symphyta. Although all sawflies have two pairs of wings their venation is often of the supposedly ancestral form and may be variable even within an individual specimen. Unlike many of their relatives in the other hymenopteran sub-order, the Apocrita, sawflies cannot sting. Figure 1 (p. 532) will enable you to decide which insects are sawflies.

Amongst the Hymenoptera, the adult Symphyta are characterised by the absence of a "wasp waist" constriction between the thorax and the abdomen—the latter being a feature of the Apocrita. All adult sawflies, except those in the family Cephidae, possess a pair of "cenchri" behind the scutellum. These come into contact with a scaly area on the underside of the forewings, holding them in place when the insect is at rest. It is thought that cephids (which also have slight signs of a constricted waist) form a link between the primitive Symphyta and the more advanced Apocrita (all of which lack cenchri). In most female sawflies the genitalia possess the "saws" which they use to cut through plant tissue in order to lay their eggs. In "wood wasps" (family Siricidae), however, the female must bore through bark in order to lay her eggs in the soft sapwood and as the bark is so tough a needle-like ovipositor has evolved rather than a saw. An ovipositor of

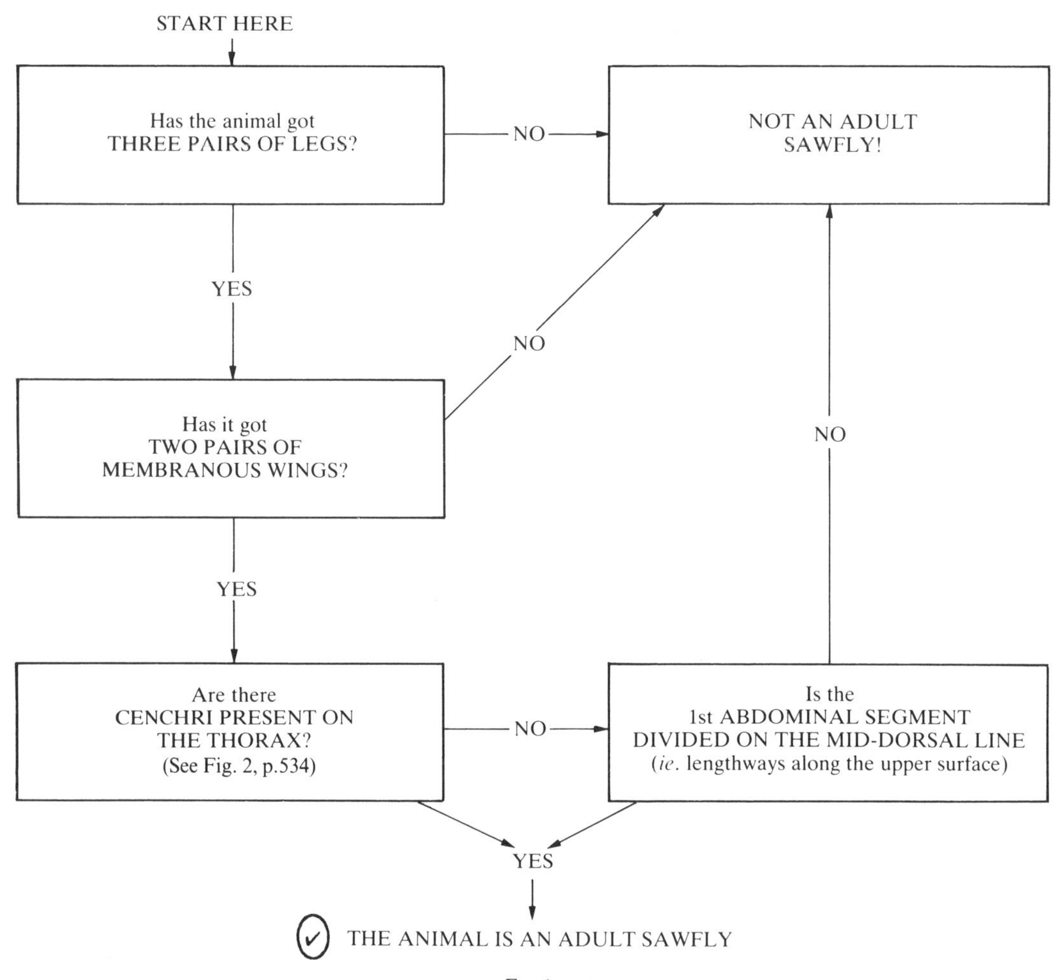

FIG. 1.
Flow-chart key to separate adult sawflies from other insects.

the type used by parasitic insects is found in the family Orussidae (but it is doubtful whether any representative of this family actually occurred in Britain).

With the exception of the Orussidae, which are parasitic in later instars, the larvae of sawflies all feed on plant material—mostly in the open on the leaves. They may feed singly (in which case they often have cryptic coloration) or gregariously (when they are frequently vividly marked). In the latter case, the larvae often rear up simultaneously when threatened, thus using "scare tactics". There is also evidence that they may produce chemical defence substances, since handling large numbers of larvae of the family Diprionidae can cause skin irritation (Forestry Commission, 1955). Some sawfly larvae have developed more specialised means of feeding, such as leaf mining, leaf rolling or even inducing gall formation in their host plant. Wood wasp larvae live in gymnosperm and angiosperm sap-wood. Several other sawfly larvae live within the stems of plants such as cereals or other grasses, woody and non-gramineous herbs.

Although individual species are usually quite specific in terms of their host plant, sawfly larvae, collectively, feed on a vast range of species from primitive plants such as horsetails and ferns, through grasses and herbaceous plants to conifers, fruit and other deciduous trees. Perhaps the most highly favoured plants are poplars and willows. However, the food plants of several British sawflies are still unknown and much work remains to be done on sawflies generally and sawfly larvae in particular.

Free-living sawfly larvae are similar in appearance to the caterpillars of Lepidoptera, but they have only one pair of eyes in contrast to the several pairs possessed by larvae of butterflies and moths. These extra eyes often appear as black spots on the lower side margins of the head. Usually, sawfly larvae have 6 or more pairs of abdominal pro-legs, whilst caterpillars never have more than 5 pairs. However, in leaf mining or stem-boring species, the legs may be reduced in number and size, and larval morphology of these types varies considerably from species to species.

Once fully grown, sawfly larvae moult to form a prepupal stage, which is of a different pattern to the larva. They then form a case or cocoon around themselves. This may be below ground in leaf litter, under soft bark or even in galls (not necessarily their own) or else attached to the stems or leaves of a living plant. The length of time spent in the prepupal stage within the cocoon varies, but may be several months. At this stage, humidity is believed to be critical and this may account for the large numbers of sawfly larvae which enter coccoons in captivity, never to emerge as adults. It seems that desiccation is a real threat in the wild, and sites offering the correct humidity levels must be chosen. A pupa is formed from the prepupa and emergence of the adult sawfly follows in due course. In Britain, most adults emerge in May and June, although some such as *Dolerus* may be seen in March, whilst *Apethymus* can be on the wing in October. Larvae of most species are full grown in late summer or autumn and are safe in their cocoons before the weather turns too cold. However, several species of sawfly have two or even three generations per year, in which case the life cycle is much accelerated.

Many adult sawflies visit flowers to feed on pollen, nectar, stamens or petals. Others, unlike their larvae, are carnivorous and capture their prey in strong jaws. They will tackle quite large insects, for example a label attached to a *Rhogogaster viridis* (L.) in the H. W. Daltry collection states that the specimen was caught in the act of eating a winter moth caterpillar *Operophtera brumata* (L.)—which would have been almost twice as long as the sawfly. If you pick up some of the larger species, such as the common black and green *Tenthredo mesomelas* (L.), you will find that they try to bite with some determination, but their jaws appear to be incapable of puncturing the skin—at least they have never drawn blood from the author yet!

The adults themselves are relatively soft-bodied when compared to other insects, although some of the cimbicids have quite a hard exoskeleton. Cimbicids are also exceptional in that some of them are strong fliers, whilst most sawflies are weak in flight. Once they emerge as adults, sawflies live only for a short while, often only a few days, although in some species adults survive for about four weeks.

The above notes form only a very brief introduction to the group and readers wishing to know more about sawflies and their habits should read Benson (1950). The section on sawflies in Gauld and Bolton (1988) is also valuable reading. Stehr (1987) includes a key to the larvae of sawfly subfamilies.

Sawfly Morphology

Identification is, of course, based upon comparison of shared features between individual species or groups of species (genera). Some of the characters used in identification are

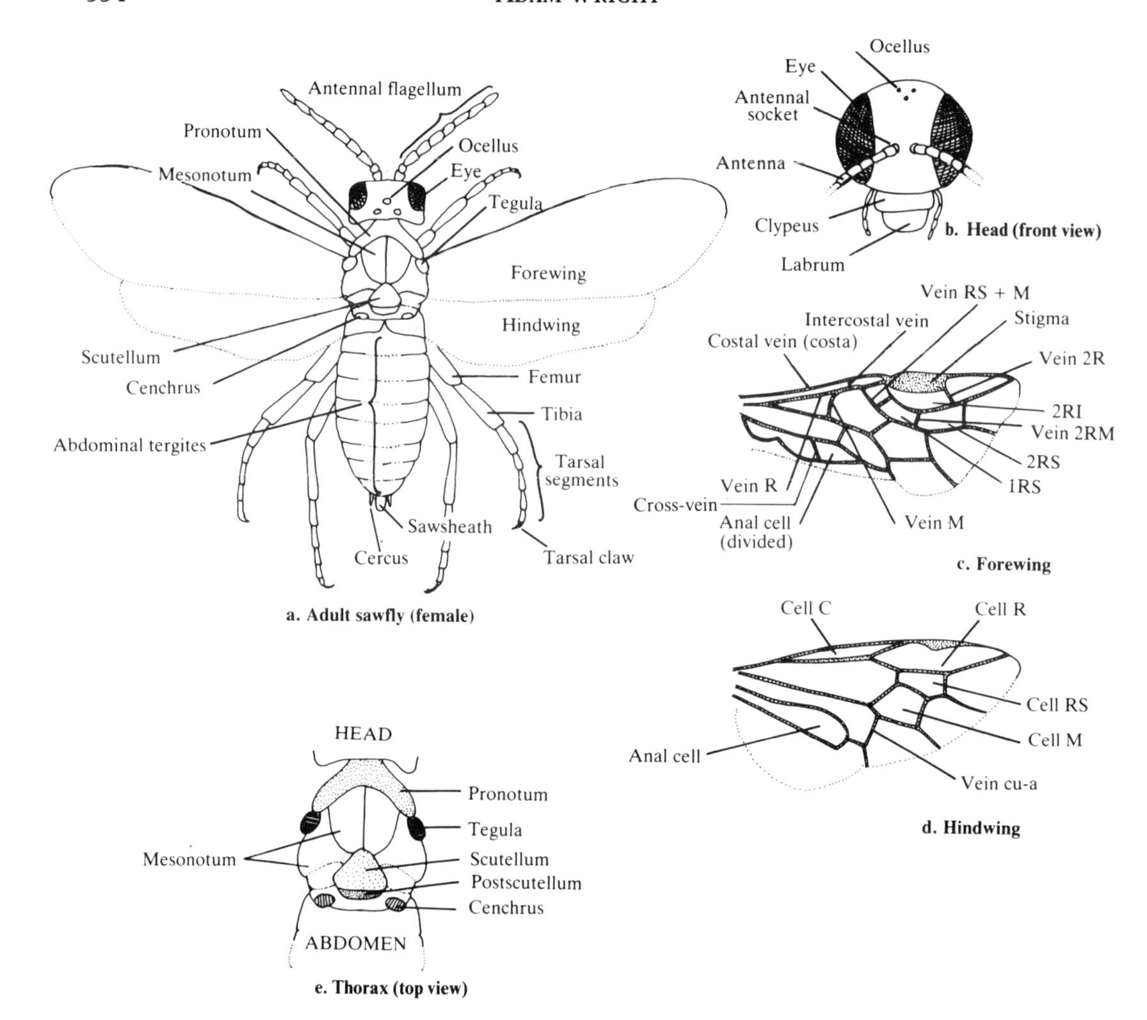

FIG. 2
External features of an adult sawfly.

unique to sawflies; these, and other features, may be described in unfamiliar terminology and, therefore, labelled diagrams of the important diagnostic parts are presented in Figure 2.

Sexing of adult sawflies is not difficult; in females the last segment of the abdomen is longitudinally divided underneath by the sheath containing the saws. The corresponding last segment of the male sawfly (which of course lacks saws) has no such division and merely forms a smooth-surfaced undercarriage.

COLLECTING AND PRESERVING SAWFLIES

During spring and summer, warm sunny days will encourage sawflies to take to the wing. Their slow, rather clumsy flight will soon be recognised and it is then easy to net individuals in flight. Searching flower heads, such as umbels or yellow composites, is often productive. Once feeding at flower heads, sawflies are often quite preoccupied and may be captured easily with the aid of a "pooter". Alternatively, they can also be netted from the flowers. I prefer the latter method, for reasons explained below.

Sweeping long grass and other foliage will often yield many species, especially of *Dolerus*. Beating trees such as willows or pines is also productive, particularly for nematines on willows and diprionids or *Xyela julii* (Brebisson) on pines. Sawflies will also frequently be seen on leaves of trees, sunbathing or even ovipositing. In such situations they can most readily be netted. Once caught, it is imperative that each sawfly should be kept separate from all others—if you put two in the same tube one may eat part of, or all of, the other! This habit is a severe disadvantage when collecting sawflies by means of a "pooter".

It may be necessary to kill and mount some specimens in order to identify them. Sawflies can be killed rapidly using ethyl acetate fumes (Note. Do not use plastic tubes as these will dissolve!). The specimens should then be pinned through the thorax. The wings and legs should be arranged so that all characters are clearly visible. Wing venation, antennae, clypeus shape and tarsal claws are all features regularly needed for identification. Genitalia preparations may also be required—these are discussed in the Appendix (p. 592). Once set, sawflies can be left to dry in the air. I then prefer to stage my specimens on polyporous or "plastazote" strips. Full data relating to the place, grid reference, date and collector, together with any other relevant data should of course be present on the label accompanying the specimen.

Although many sawflies retain their natural colours once preserved, quite a few tend to suffer from colour fading. Such colour changes are most marked in green species such as some *Nematus* spp. and *Strombocerus delicatulus*. Upon preservation, the bright green soon fades to a dull straw colour.

In comparison to many other British insect groups, our knowledge of sawflies is still in its infancy. It was not until 1987 that the informal "Sawfly Study Group" was set up to produce a newsletter for information exchange. It is hoped that this group will lead to the start of a national recording scheme for sawflies. Anyone interested in joining the Sawfly Study Group should write to me.

Using the Keys

Many sawflies are small creatures and many of the features used in identification, certainly at species level, are, therefore, very small. A microscope is necessary to identify them satisfactorily. For most characters X45 magnification is perfectly adequate, but in order to study teeth on saws in critical species X90 magnification is required. However, a X10 hand lens will enable you to reach family level at least and in some instances go considerably further.

The key is intended to provide a simple means of getting to grips with the British sawfly genera, as an alternative to Benson's highly accurate, but sometimes hard to use, Royal Entomological Society Keys (1951, 1952, 1958). However, because sawflies are primitive Hymenoptera, subject to a certain amount of aberrant wing venation and/or to other abnormalities, specimens will occur which do not key out in the present work. Occasionally, these may key out to the wrong genus. However, the only way to cover all eventualities is to include the long lists of "catch-all" combinations used by Benson, which would defeat the purpose of the present work.

I hope those unfortunate enough to encounter aberrant specimens causing trouble in this way will forgive me. I am prepared to look at problem material by arrangement.

Confirmatory notes for each family and genus are included at the end of the keys (p. 581). They include reference numbers which should enable you to quickly cross-refer between the keys and the corresponding notes.

IDENTIFICATION GUIDES TO THE BRITISH SAWFLIES

The works of Benson (1951, 1952 and 1958), prepared for the Royal Entomological Society of London, remain the standard keys for identification of British sawflies to species level. Quinlan and Gauld (1981) updated "section (a)" of Benson's work, dealing with the families other than Tenthredinidae. Their work also provided a key to mature sawfly larvae at family level.

During the preparation of these simplified AIDGAP keys the author has drawn heavily on the above works, which I would recommend to all prospective sawfly students. Unfortunately, "section (b)" of Benson's work is now out of print.

Cameron's four-volume Ray Society publication on "British Phytophagous Hymenoptera" (1882–1893) includes many illustrations of sawfly larvae, but for large numbers of British sawflies little or nothing is known about their larval stages.

RECENT TAXONOMIC CHANGES OR ADDITIONS TO THE BRITISH SAWFLY FAUNA

Since the publication of the works by Benson (1951, 1952, 1958) and by Quinlan and Gauld (1981), sixteen species of sawfly have been added to the British list. One of these included the addition of a new genus, *Endophytus*.

Taxonomic changes have resulted in the splitting of the genus *Monophadnoides* into *Monophadnoides* and *Claremontia*. Similarly, the genus *Melisandra* used by Benson has been divided into *Nesoselandria* and *Birka*.

Benson (1960) gave characters for separating adults of the genera *Pontania* and *Phyllocolpa*.

Tenthredo perkinsi (Morice) was deleted from the revised Hymenoptera checklist (Fitton *et al.*, 1978), but has been re-instated as the valid species *T. notha* Klug (Taeger, 1985). Taeger's revision of *Tenthredo*, also includes the "new" species *T. pseudorossii* Taeger which is the *T. rossii* (Panzer) of Benson's work.

Also lost in the Fitton *et al.* (1978) Hymenoptera checklist revision was *Tenthredopsis friesii* Konow, which current information suggests should be re-instated (D. A. Sheppard, *personal communication*).

The sixteen species added to the British lists since publication of Benson's Royal Entomological Society keys are listed below, together with relevant references.

Xiphydria longicollis (Geoffroy)	Shaw and Liston (1987).
Macrophya alboannulata (Costa)	Liston (1983a).
Macrophya parvula Konow	Liston (1987).
Endophytus anemones (Hering)	Benson (1961a).
Pristiphora coactula (Ruthe)	Benson (1959).
Pristiphora decipiens Enslin	Liston (1981a); Benes and Kristek (1976).
Pristiphora pseudodecipiens	Benes & Kristek (1976).
Pristiphora karvoneni (Lindqvist).	Liston (1983b).

Pristiphora lanifica (Zaddach & Brischke)	Liston (1981b).
Pristiphora micronematica Malaise	Liston (1982).
Amauronematus kamtchatica Malaise	Lindqvist (1961).
Amauronematus godmani Benson	Benson (1959).
Pachynematus arcticus (Lindqvist)	Benson (1961b).
Pachynematus glabriceps Lindqvist	Benson (1964).
Pachynematus torridonensis	Liston (1980a).
Pachynematus virginalis	Liston (1980).

CLASSIFICATION LIST OF BRITISH HYMENOPTERA: SYMPHYTA

Numbers in brackets after each genus denote the number of species currently recognised as British

Family XYELIDAE
- *Xyela* (2)

Family PAMPHILIIDAE
- *Acantholyda* (2)
- *Cephalcia* (1)
- *Neurotoma* (2)
- *Pamphilius* (14)

Family MEGALODONTIDAE
- *Megalodontes* (3) (all doubtful as genuine British species)

Family XIPHYDRIIDAE
- *Xiphydria* (3)

Family SIRICIDAE
- *Urocerus* (5)
- *Sirex* (4)
- *Xeris* (1)
- *Tremex* (1)

Family ORUSSIDAE
- *Orussus* (1) (not recorded in Britain for 150 years)

Family CEPHIDAE
- *Hartigia* (3)
- *Janus* (2)
- *Cephus* (2)
- *Trachelus* (2) (one of which has not been recorded in Britain for 150 years)
- *Calameuta* (2)

Family ARGIDAE
- *Aprosthema* (1)
- *Sterictophora* (2)
- *Arge* (12)

Family BLASTICOTOMIDAE
- *Blasticotoma* (1)

Family CIMBICIDAE
- *Corynis* (2) (both doubtfully British)
- *Zaraea* (3)
- *Abia* (2)
- *Cimbex* (3)
- *Pseudoclavellaria* (1) (doubtfully British)
- *Trichiosoma* (?3) (taxonomic status of other forms uncertain)

Family DIPRIONIDAE
- *Monoctenus* (1)
- *Microdiprion* (1)
- *Neodiprion* (1)
- *Diprion* (2)
- *Gilpinia* (4)

Family TENTHREDINIDAE

Subfamily SELANDRIINAE
- *Heptamelus* (1)
- *Pseudohemitaxonus* (1)
- *Strombocerus* (1)
- *Strongylogaster* (6) (of which two are dubious as British species)
- *Aneugmenus* (3)
- *Nesoselandria* (1)
- *Birka* (1)
- *Brachythops* (2)
- *Selandria* (2)
- *Loderus* (3)
- *Dolerus* (28)

Subfamily Heterarthrinae
- *Heterarthrus* (5)

Subfamily Blennocampinae
- *Athalia* (10)
- *Harpiphorus* (1)
- *Monostegia* (1)
- *Monosoma* (1)
- *Empria* (13)
- *Ametastegia* (3)
- *Protemphytus* (4)
- *Taxonus* (1)
- *Allantus* (9)
- *Apethymus* (2)
- *Endelomyia* (1)
- *Caliroa* (4)
- *Tomostethus* (1)
- *Eutomostethus* (4)
- *Stethomostus* (2)
- *Phymatocera* (1)
- *Rhadinoceraea* (1)
- *Dicrostema* (1)
- *Monophadnus* (1)
- *Periclista* (30)
- *Ardis* (2)
- *Pareophora* (1)
- *Blennocampa* (1)
- *Cladardis* (1) (doubtfully British)
- *Monophadnoides* (2)
- *Claremontia* (4)
- *Halidamia* (1)
- *Parna* (1)
- *Metallus* (3)
- *Scolioneura* (1)
- *Messa* (3)
- *Profenusa* (2)
- *Fenusa* (3)
- *Fenella* (2)

Subfamily Tenthredininae
- *Eriocampa* (1)
- *Perineura* (1)
- *Aglaostigma* (2)
- *Tenthredopsis* (5)
- *Sciapteryx* (2)
- *Rhogogaster* (7)
- *Tenthredo* (26)
- *Pachyprotasis* (5)
- *Macrophya* (11)

Subfamily Nematinae
- *Cladius* (2)
- *Priophorus* (5)
- *Trichiocampus* (1)
- *Hoplocampa* (9)
- *Hemichroa* (2)
- *Anoplonyx* (1)
- *Platycampus* (1)
- *Dineura* (3)
- *Mesoneura* (1)
- *Pseudodineura* (2)
- *Endophytus* (1)
- *Stauronematus* (1)
- *Pristiphora* (50)
- *Amauronematus* (23)
- *Nematinus* (5)
- *Euura* (5)
- *Phyllocolpa* (10)
- *Pontania* (12)
- *Croesus* (4)
- *Nematus* (40)
- *Pachynematus* (21)

GLOSSARY

CARINA: A keel-like ridge. Many sawflies have such a keel around the upper hind margin of the head.

CENCHRUS: A small, paired projection on a sawfly's thorax, situated near the scutellum (Fig. 2e, p. 534). The cenchri come into contact with a scaly area on the underside of the forewings, holding the wings in place when the insect is at rest.

CLYPEUS: A hard plate at the front of the insect's head, immediately above the labrum (Fig. 2b, p. 534).

COSTA: The thickened vein at the leading edge of an insect's wing (Fig. 2c, p. 534).

INSTAR: A particular stage in an insect's life, covering the period between one moult and the next. Reference is usually made to larval instars.

LABRUM: The plate at the front of the insect's head, bordering the mouthparts (Fig. 2b, p. 534). Effectively the insect's top lip.

MESONOTUM: The central dorsal region of the thorax (Fig. 2e, p. 534).

POOTER: Apparatus for collecting insects, consisting of a cylinder into which insects are sucked by means of a tube. Note that sawflies will eat each other (and other insects) in a confined space.

PRONOTUM: The front dorsal region of an insect's thorax, immediately behind the head (Fig. 2e, p. 534)

SCUTELLUM: The subcircular or triangular region of an insect's thorax, situated at the rear of the thorax on its dorsal surface (Fig. 2e, p. 534).

STERNITE: A plate forming the under surface of an abdominal segment.

STIGMA: A thickened area on the leading edge of the forewing of an insect (Fig. 2c, p. 534).

TEGULA: A small, semicircular plate situated above the base of each forewing (Fig. 2e, p. 534).

TERGITE: A plate forming the dorsal surface of an abdominal segment (Fig. 2a, p. 534).

KEY 1

A Key to the Families of British Sawflies

Where a family has only one British genus, the confirmatory check characters are given in this key. In all other cases, the check characters are given at the beginning of the following keys

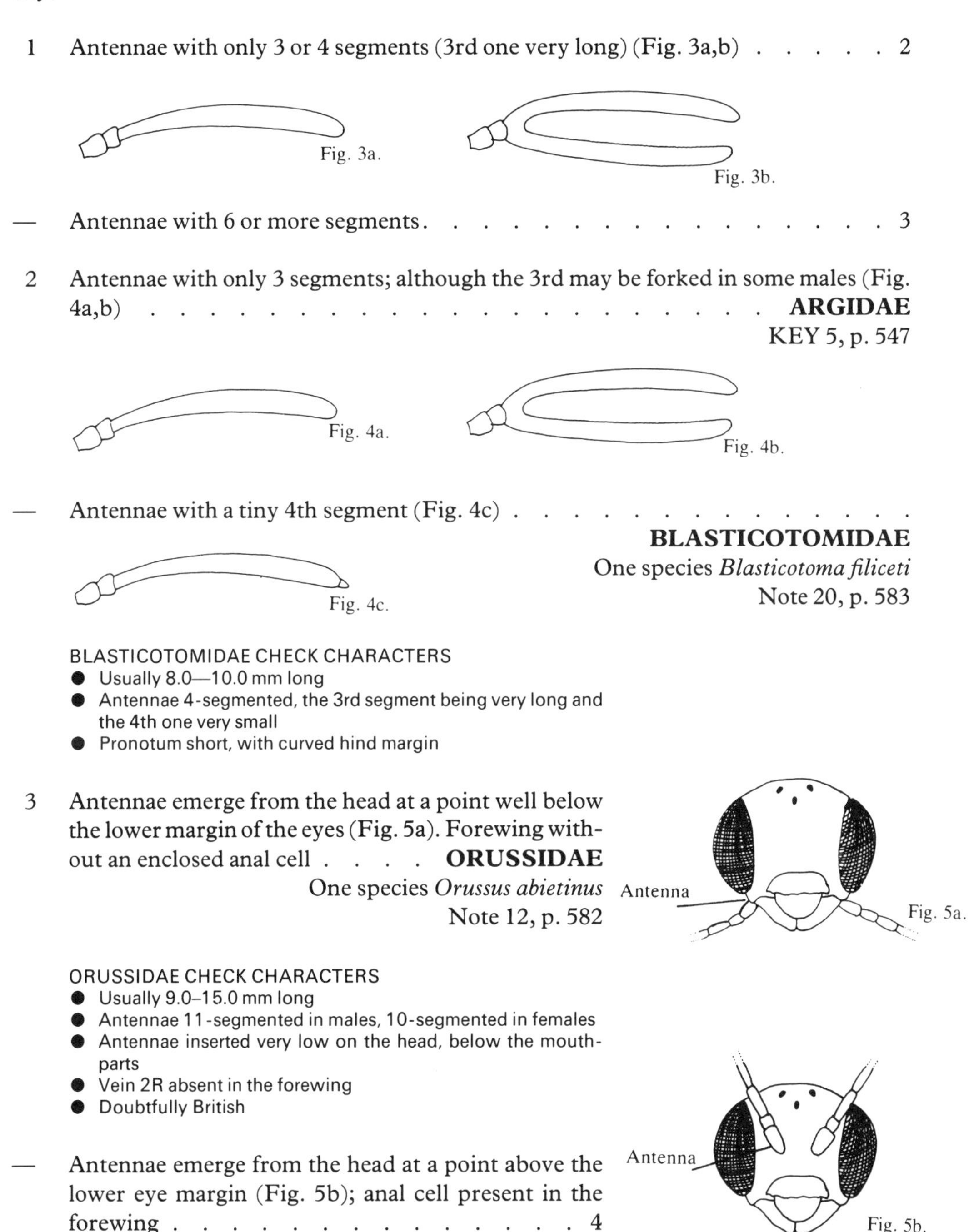

1 Antennae with only 3 or 4 segments (3rd one very long) (Fig. 3a,b) 2

Fig. 3a. Fig. 3b.

— Antennae with 6 or more segments. 3

2 Antennae with only 3 segments; although the 3rd may be forked in some males (Fig. 4a,b) . . . . **ARGIDAE**
KEY 5, p. 547

Fig. 4a. Fig. 4b.

— Antennae with a tiny 4th segment (Fig. 4c) . . . .
BLASTICOTOMIDAE
One species *Blasticotoma filiceti*
Note 20, p. 583

Fig. 4c.

BLASTICOTOMIDAE CHECK CHARACTERS
- Usually 8.0—10.0 mm long
- Antennae 4-segmented, the 3rd segment being very long and the 4th one very small
- Pronotum short, with curved hind margin

3 Antennae emerge from the head at a point well below the lower margin of the eyes (Fig. 5a). Forewing without an enclosed anal cell . . . . **ORUSSIDAE**
One species *Orussus abietinus*
Note 12, p. 582

Fig. 5a.

ORUSSIDAE CHECK CHARACTERS
- Usually 9.0–15.0 mm long
- Antennae 11-segmented in males, 10-segmented in females
- Antennae inserted very low on the head, below the mouthparts
- Vein 2R absent in the forewing
- Doubtfully British

— Antennae emerge from the head at a point above the lower eye margin (Fig. 5b); anal cell present in the forewing 4

Fig. 5b.

4 Antennae composed of 3 large basal segments, followed by a thin filament of a further 9 segments (Fig. 6a). Whole insect 5 mm long or less . . . .

XYELIDAE
One genus *Xyela*
Note 1, p. 581

Fig. 6a.

XYELIDAE CHECK CHARACTERS

- Usually 2.5–4.5 mm long
- Antennae of three "normal" segments, followed by a slender filament of 9 or so tiny segments
- Pronotum long, with a straight hind margin
- Spring flying insects, associated with scot's pine

— Antennae filamentous throughout, or clubbed, or with flanges, but not as described above. Whole insect often over 5 mm long (Fig. 6b–f) 5

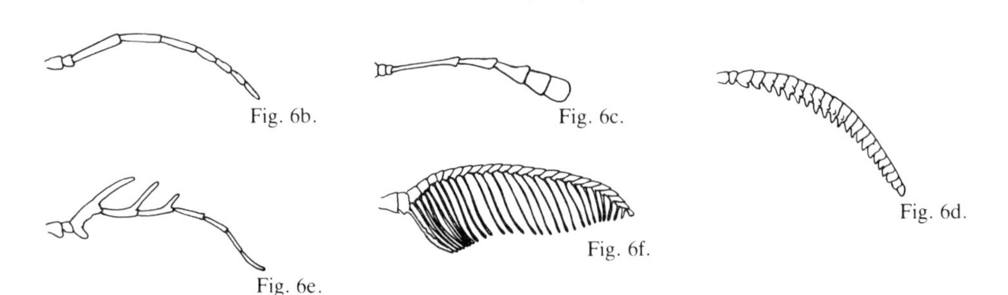

Fig. 6b. Fig. 6c. Fig. 6d. Fig. 6e. Fig. 6f.

5 Hind edge of the pronotum (excluding tegulae) is almost straight (Fig. 7a, b) . . 6

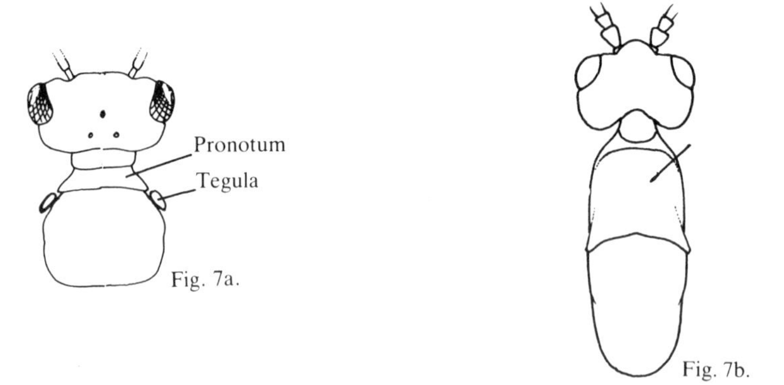

Fig. 7a. Fig. 7b.

— Hind edge of the pronotum (excluding tegulae) is obviously not straight (Fig. 7c, d) 8

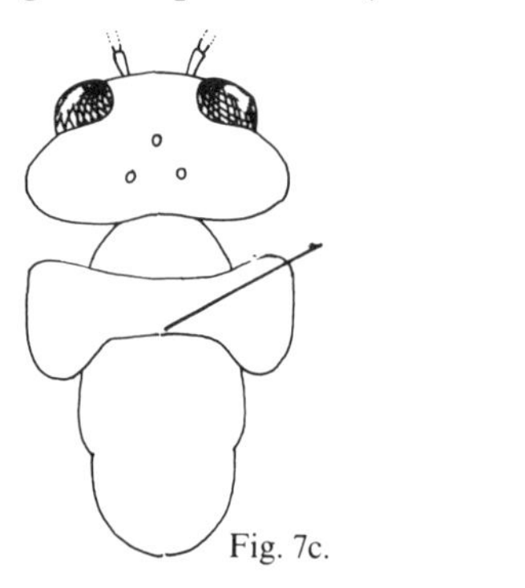

Fig. 7c.

Fig. 7d.

6 Slender insect, body cylindrical or laterally (side-to-side) compressed . . . . **CEPHIDAE**
KEY 4, p. 545

— Broad-bodied insect, body flattened dorso-ventrally (top-to-bottom). 7

7 Second abdominal tergite is divided along the mid-dorsal line (Fig. 8a) . . . . **PAMPHILIIDAE**
KEY 2, p. 543

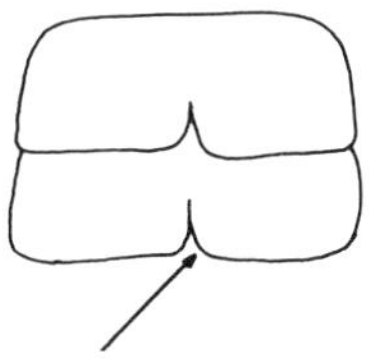

Fig. 8a.

— Second abdominal tergite is not divided along the mid-dorsal line (Fig. 8b) . **MEGALODONTIDAE**
One genus *Megalodontes*
Note 6, p. 581

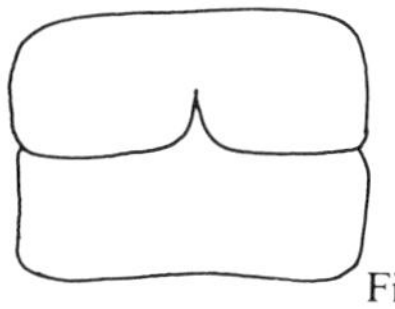

Fig. 8b.

MEGALODONTIDAE CHECK CHARACTERS
- Usually 10.0–13.0 mm long
- Antennae many-segmented, with flattened apical extensions to some segments
- Body strongly top-to-bottom (dorso-ventrally) flattened
- Wasp mimics with yellow/brown marked wings
- Doubtfully British

8 Antennae with 7 or fewer segments and ending in a club (Fig. 9) . . . . **CIMBICIDAE**
KEY 6, p. 548

Fig. 9.

— Antennae with more than 7 segments. 9

9 Front tibiae with only one apical spur (Fig. 10a), or with two spurs differing greatly in size (Fig. 10b) (look carefully) 10

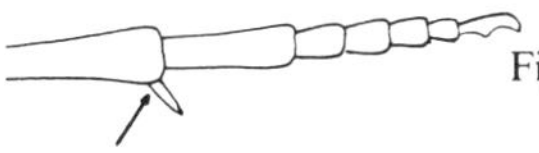

Fig. 10a.

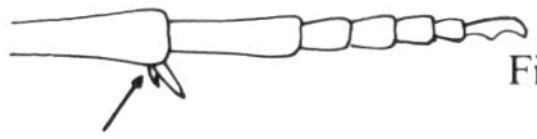

Fig. 10b.

— Front tibiae with two apical spurs of roughly equal size (Fig. 10c) 11

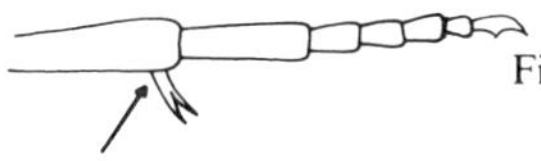

Fig. 10c.

10 Pronotum, when seen from above, shaped like a bow tie (Fig. 11a) . . . . **SIRICIDAE**
KEY 3, p. 544

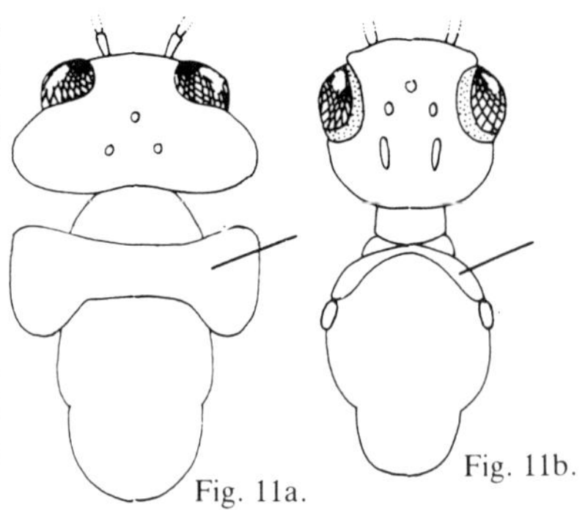

— Pronotum, when seen from above, cap shaped (Fig. 11b) . . . . **XIPHYDRIIDAE**
One genus *Xiphydria*
Note 7, p. 581

Fig. 11a. Fig. 11b.

XIPHYDRIIDAE CHECK CHARACTERS

- Usually over 14 mm long
- Antennae with 13–19 segments
- Head almost spherical in appearance, with long neck

11 Antennae with 17–23 segments (these have feathery projections in males) (Figs. 12a,b) . **DIPRIONIDAE**
KEY 7, p. 550

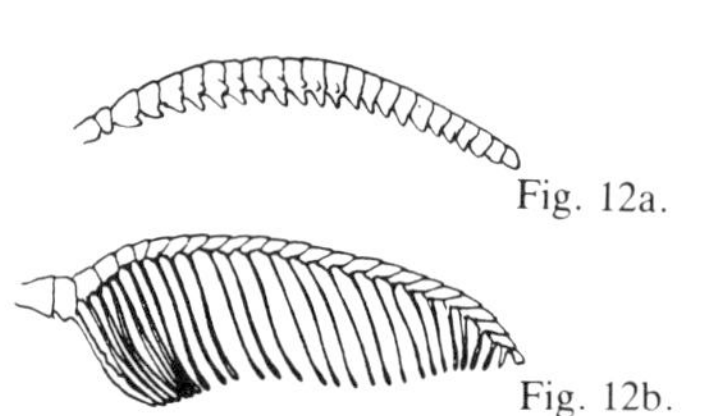
Fig. 12a.
Fig. 12b.

— Antennae with 15 or fewer segments (usually 9) (Figs. 12c,d) . . . . **TENTHREDINIDAE**
KEY 8, p. 552

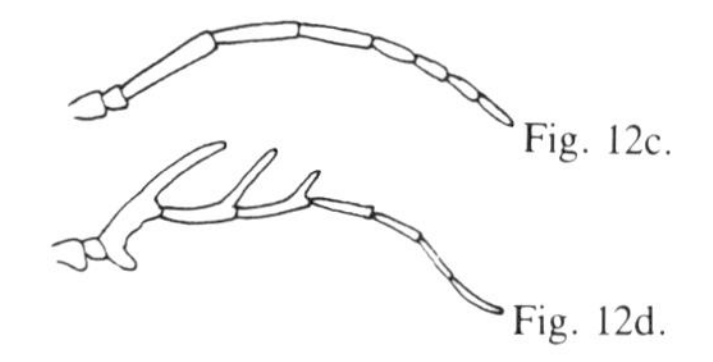
Fig. 12c.
Fig. 12d.

KEY 2

Key to the Genera of British Pamphiliidae

- Usually 7.0–15.0 mm long
- Antennae 18–24 segments
- 1st and 2nd abdominal tergites split on mid-line
- Body top-to-bottom (dorso-ventrally) flattened

1 Tarsal claws bifid (two toothed) with inner tooth well developed (Fig. 13a) (look carefully) 2

Fig. 13a.

— Tarsal claws bifid but with the inner tooth very small (Fig. 13b) (look carefully) 3

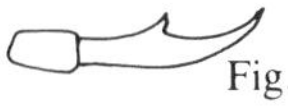

Fig. 13b.

2 Subcostal vein of the forewing joins the costa (Fig. 14a) . . . . *Pamphilius*
Note 5, p. 581

— Subcostal vein of the forewing does not touch the costa (Fig. 14b) . . . . *Neurotoma*
Note 4, p. 581

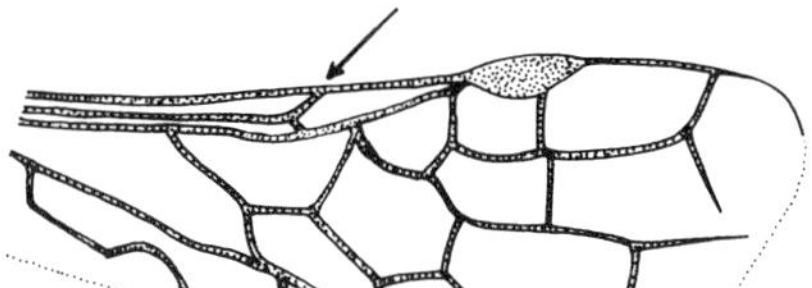

Fig. 14a.

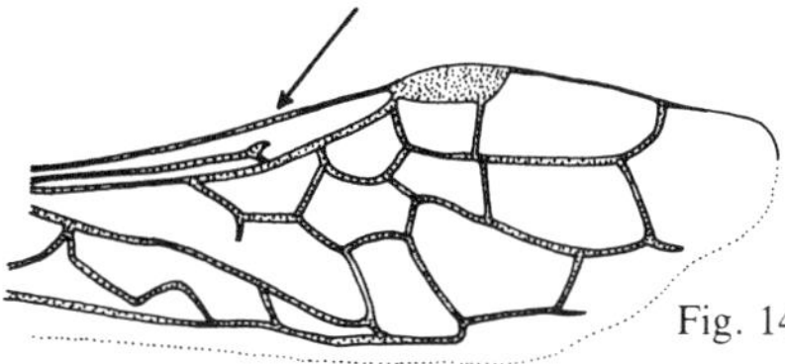

Fig. 14b.

3 Front tibia with a pre-apical spine as well as apical spurs (Fig. 15a). . . . . *Acantholyda*
Note 2, p. 581

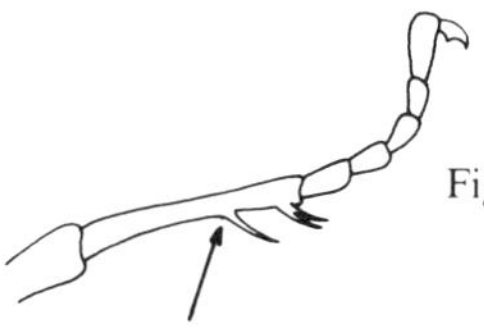

Fig. 15a.

— Front tibia with apical spurs, but lacking pre-apical spine (Fig. 15b) . . . . *Cephalcia*
Note 3, p. 581

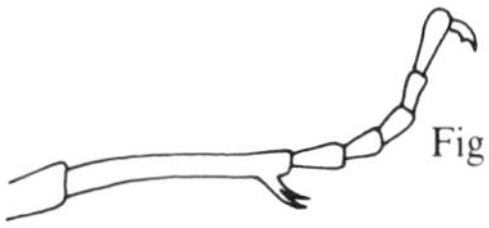

Fig. 15b.

KEY 3

KEY TO THE GENERA OF BRITISH SIRICIDAE

- Usually over 14.0 mm long
- Antennae with 14–30 segments
- Last abdominal sternite with horn-like projection

1 Forewing with vein **2RM** absent (Fig. 16a) . . *Tremex*
Note 11, p. 582

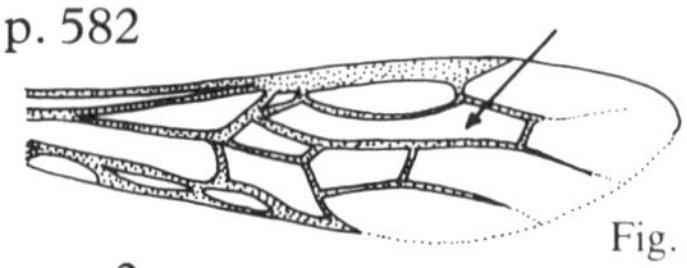

Fig. 16a.

— Forewing with vein **2RM** present (Fig. 16b) 2

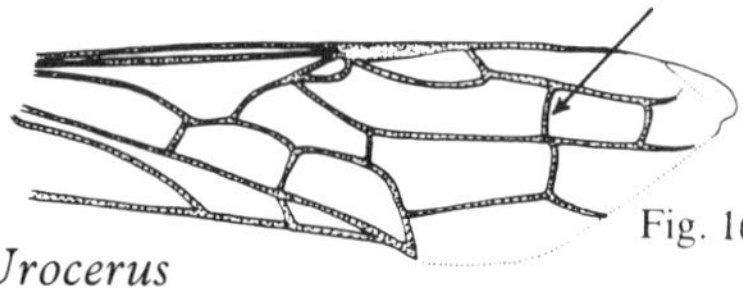

Fig. 16b.

2 Antennae pale yellow or whitish, at least in part . *Urocerus*
Note 8, p. 582

— Antennae dark brown or black throughout 3

3 Pronotum all dark . . . . *Sirex*
Note 9, p. 582

— Pronotum two-tone: dark with pale lateral stripes . *Xeris*
Note 10, p. 582

KEY 4

A Key to the Genera of British Cephidae

- Usually 4.0–18.0 mm long
- Antennae with 16–30 segments
- Cenchri absent
- Pronotum large, hind margin almost straight
- First abdominal tergite with a deep central division leaving a large triangular, pale area

1 Antennal segment 3 longer than segment 4 (start counting with segment 1 closest to the head) 2

— Antennal segment 3 shorter than or equal to segment 4. 3

2 Hind tibia with a single pre-apical spine (Fig. 17a) *Hartigia*
Note 13, p. 582

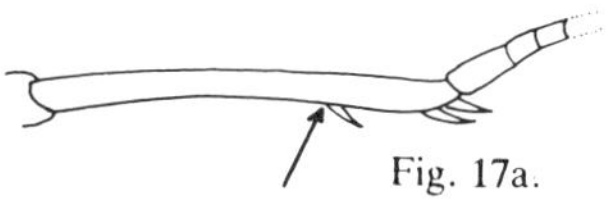

Fig. 17a.

— Hind tibia with a pair of pre-apical spines (Fig. 17b) (look carefully from several angles) . . . . *Janus*
Note 14, p. 582

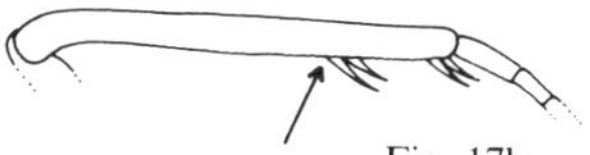

Fig. 17b.

3 Sawsheath absent (Fig. 18a) (view abdomen from the side) (MALES) 4

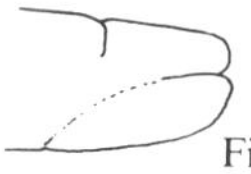

Fig. 18a.

— Sawsheath present (Fig. 18b) (view abdomen from the side) (FEMALES) 6

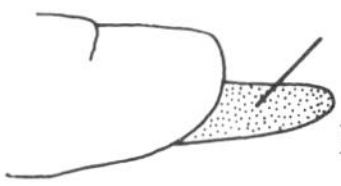

Fig. 18b.

4 7th and 8th abdominal sternites each with a deep pit (Fig. 19a) (view the underside of the abdomen) . . *Trachelus*
Note 16, p. 582

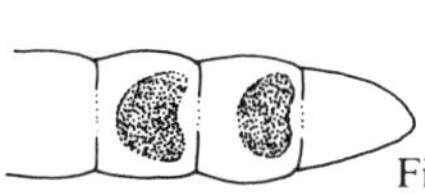

Fig. 19a.

— No such pits present on the 7th and 8th abdominal sternites (Fig. 19b) (view the underside of the abdomen) . . . 5

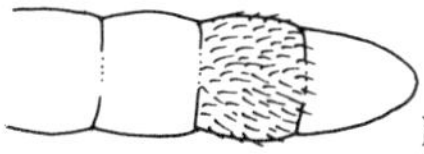

Fig. 19b.

5 8th abdominal sternite with a triangular hair patch and an apical row of large, flattened setae (best seen as dark hairs in side view) (Fig. 20a) . . . . *Cephus*
Note 15, p. 582

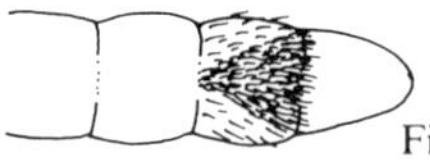

Fig. 20a.

— 8th abdominal sternite without an unusually hairy triangular patch (Fig. 20b); apical setae neither flattened or enlarged . . . . *Calameuta*
Note 15, p. 582

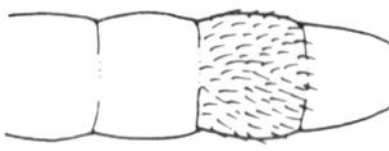

Fig. 20b.

6 In side view, the cerci reach virtually to the end of the sawsheath (Fig. 21a) . . . . *Calameuta*
Note 15, p. 582

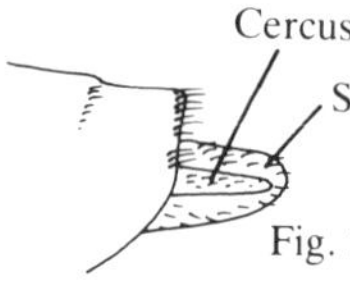

Cercus
Sawsheath
Fig. 21a.

— In side view, the cerci are clearly much shorter than the sawsheath (Fig. 21b) 7

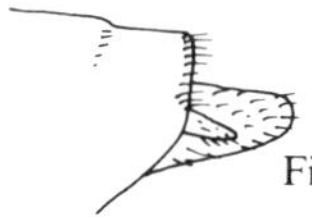

Fig. 21b.

7 Viewed from above, the sawsheath tapers at its tip (Fig. 22a) . . . . *Cephus*
Note 15, p. 582

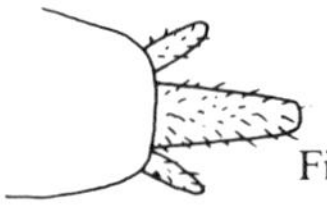

Fig. 22a.

— Viewed from above, the sawsheath expands slightly near the tip (Fig. 22b) . . . . *Trachelus*
Note 16, p. 582

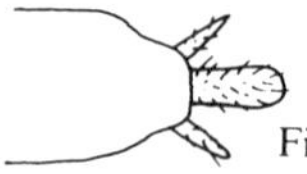

Fig. 22b.

KEY 5

A Key to the Genera of British Argidae

- Usually 5.0–11.0 mm long
- Antennae with 3 segments (3rd segment is very long)
- Third antennal segment forked in male *Sterictiphora* and *Aprosthema*
- Broad-bodied insects

Note: The illustrations given here show only the part of the wing venation which is useful for identification purposes. Real specimens will have more complex venation.

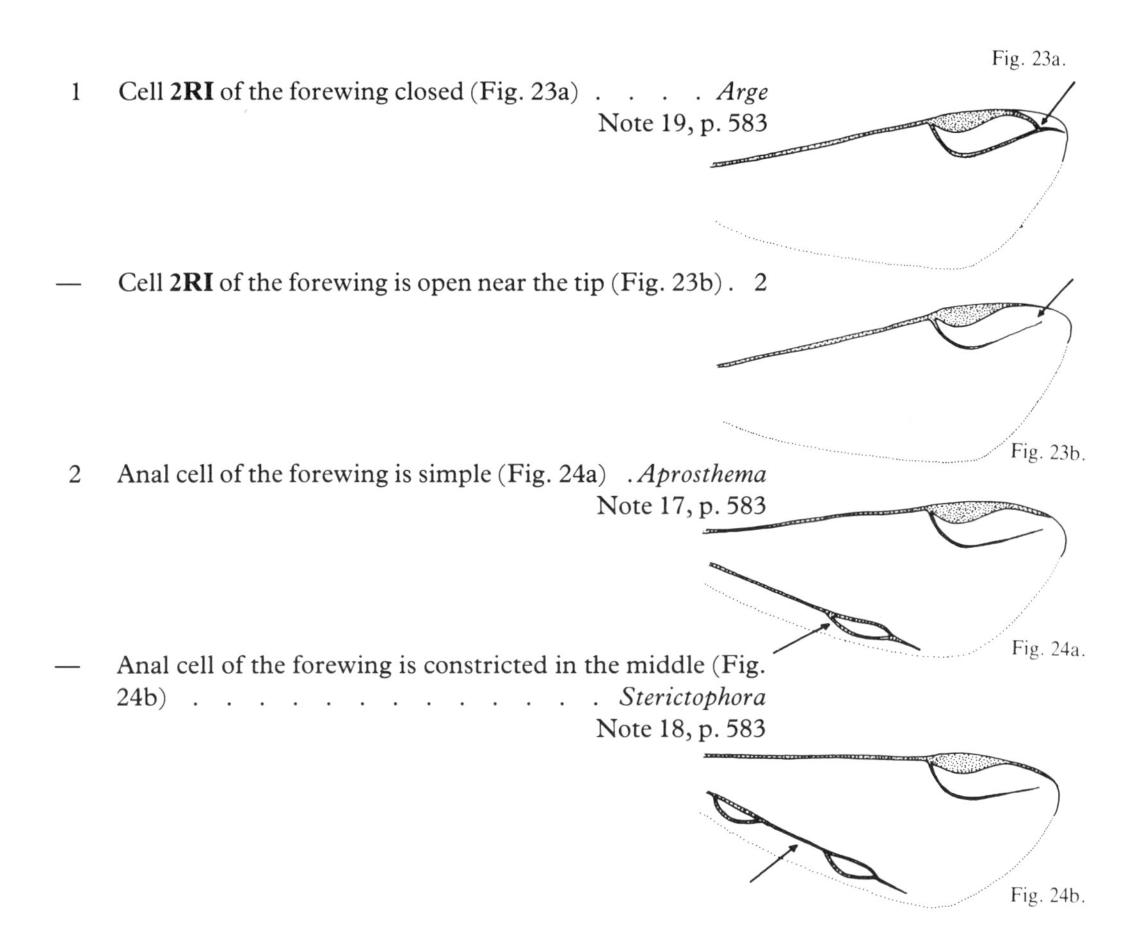

1 Cell **2RI** of the forewing closed (Fig. 23a) . . . . *Arge*
Note 19, p. 583

— Cell **2RI** of the forewing is open near the tip (Fig. 23b) . 2

2 Anal cell of the forewing is simple (Fig. 24a) . *Aprosthema*
Note 17, p. 583

— Anal cell of the forewing is constricted in the middle (Fig. 24b) . . . . *Sterictophora*
Note 18, p. 583

Fig. 23a.

Fig. 23b.

Fig. 24a.

Fig. 24b.

KEY 6

A KEY TO THE GENERA OF BRITISH CIMBICIDAE

- Usually 9.0–28.0 mm long (the doubtfully British genus *Corynis* contains species under 8.0 mm long)
- Antennae with 7 or less segments, ending in a club
- Stoutly built insects

Note: The illustrations given here show only the part of the wing venation which is useful for identification purposes. Real specimens will have more complex venation.

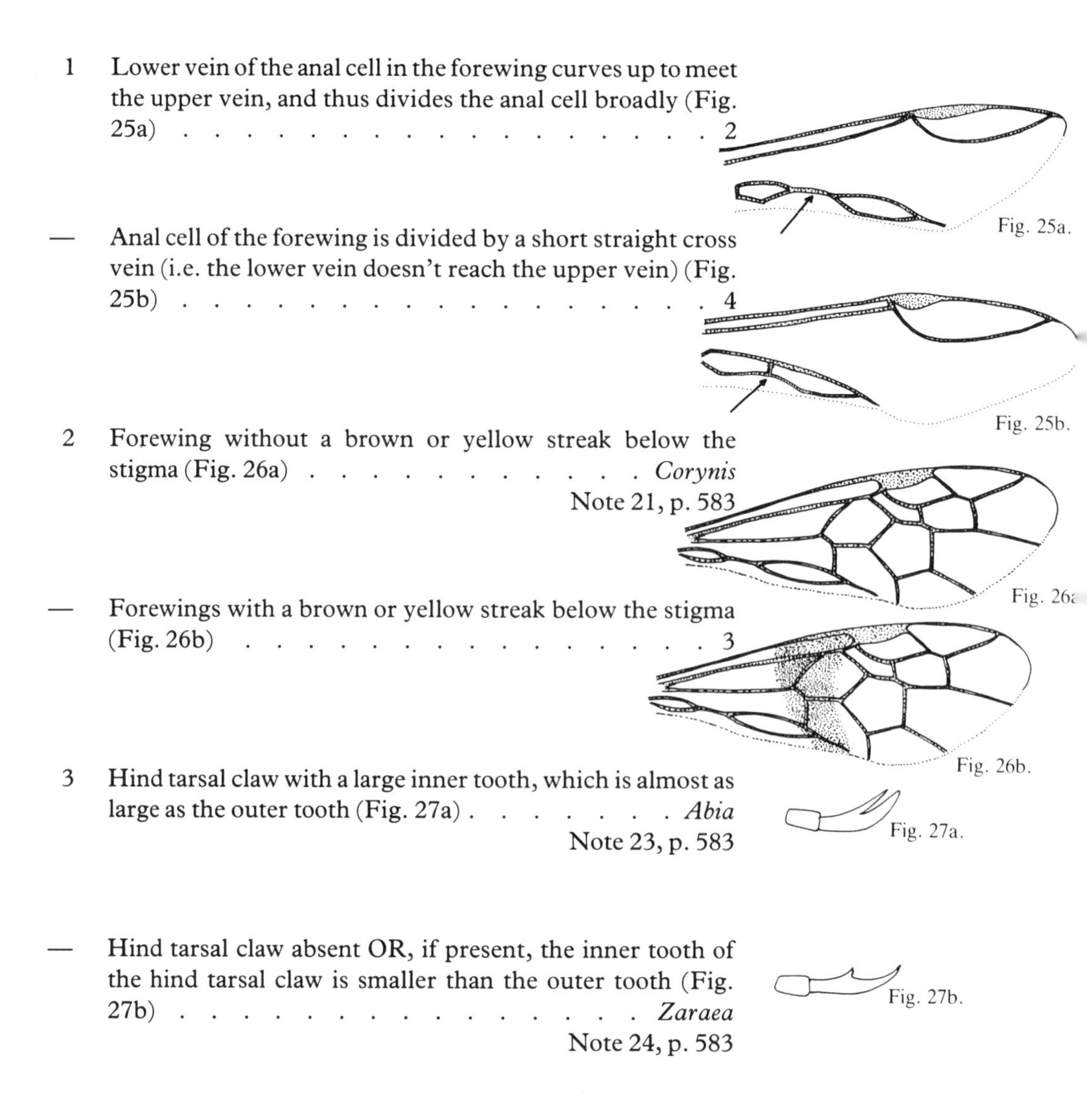

1 Lower vein of the anal cell in the forewing curves up to meet the upper vein, and thus divides the anal cell broadly (Fig. 25a) 2

— Anal cell of the forewing is divided by a short straight cross vein (i.e. the lower vein doesn't reach the upper vein) (Fig. 25b) 4

Fig. 25a.

Fig. 25b.

2 Forewing without a brown or yellow streak below the stigma (Fig. 26a) . . . . *Corynis*
Note 21, p. 583

— Forewings with a brown or yellow streak below the stigma (Fig. 26b) 3

Fig. 26a.

Fig. 26b.

3 Hind tarsal claw with a large inner tooth, which is almost as large as the outer tooth (Fig. 27a) . . . . *Abia*
Note 23, p. 583

Fig. 27a.

— Hind tarsal claw absent OR, if present, the inner tooth of the hind tarsal claw is smaller than the outer tooth (Fig. 27b) . . . . *Zaraea*
Note 24, p. 583

Fig. 27b.

4 First abdominal segment (as seen from above) is arched behind to expose a large pale area (Fig. 28a) . . *Cimbex*
Notes 22 & 25, p. 583

Fig. 28a.

— First abdominal segment is not arched behind (as seen from above) (Fig. 28b) 5

Fig. 28b.

5 Hind femur with a subapical tooth (Fig. 29a) *Trichiosoma*
Notes 22 & 25, p. 583

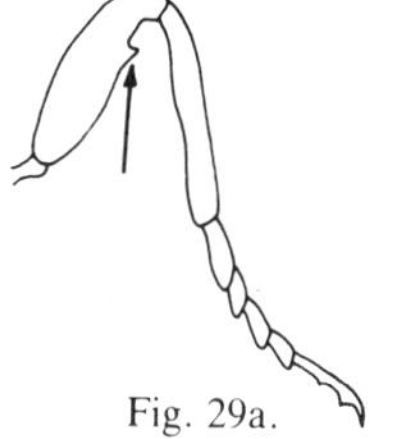
Fig. 29a.

— Hind femur without a tooth (Fig. 29b) . *Pseudoclavellaria*
Note 21, p. 583

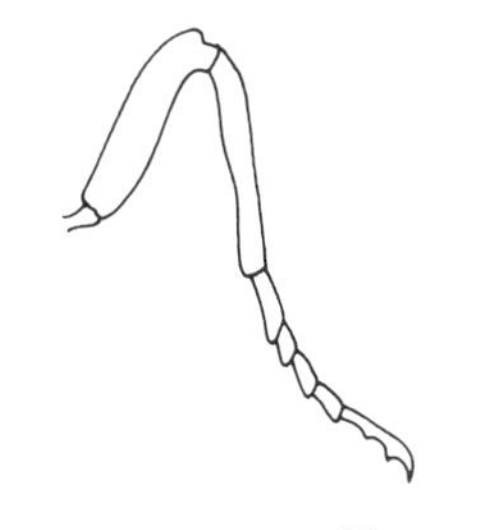
Fig. 29b.

KEY 7

A KEY TO THE BRITISH GENERA OF THE FAMILY DIPRIONIDAE

- Usually 5.0–10.0 mm long
- Antennae with at least 9 segments, and usually more (up to 22 segments)
- Males with prolongations to antennal segments
- Vein 2R missing in the forewing
- Stout-bodied, slow-flying insects associated with conifers and juniper

Note: The illustrations given here show only the part of the wing venation which is useful for identification purposes. Real specimens will have more complex venation.

1 The lower vein of the anal cell in the forewing curves up to meet the upper vein, thus dividing the anal cell (Fig. 30a) . . . . *Monoctenus*
Note 26, p. 584

— The anal cell of the forewing is divided by a short straight cross vein, not as described above (Fig. 30b) 2

2 Vein **cu-a** of the hind wing joins vein **1A** about its own length away from the tip of the anal cell (Fig. 31a); abdomen shiny 3

— Vein **cu-a** of the hind wing joins vein **1A** about twice its own length away from the tip of the anal cell (Fig. 31b); abdomen dull 4

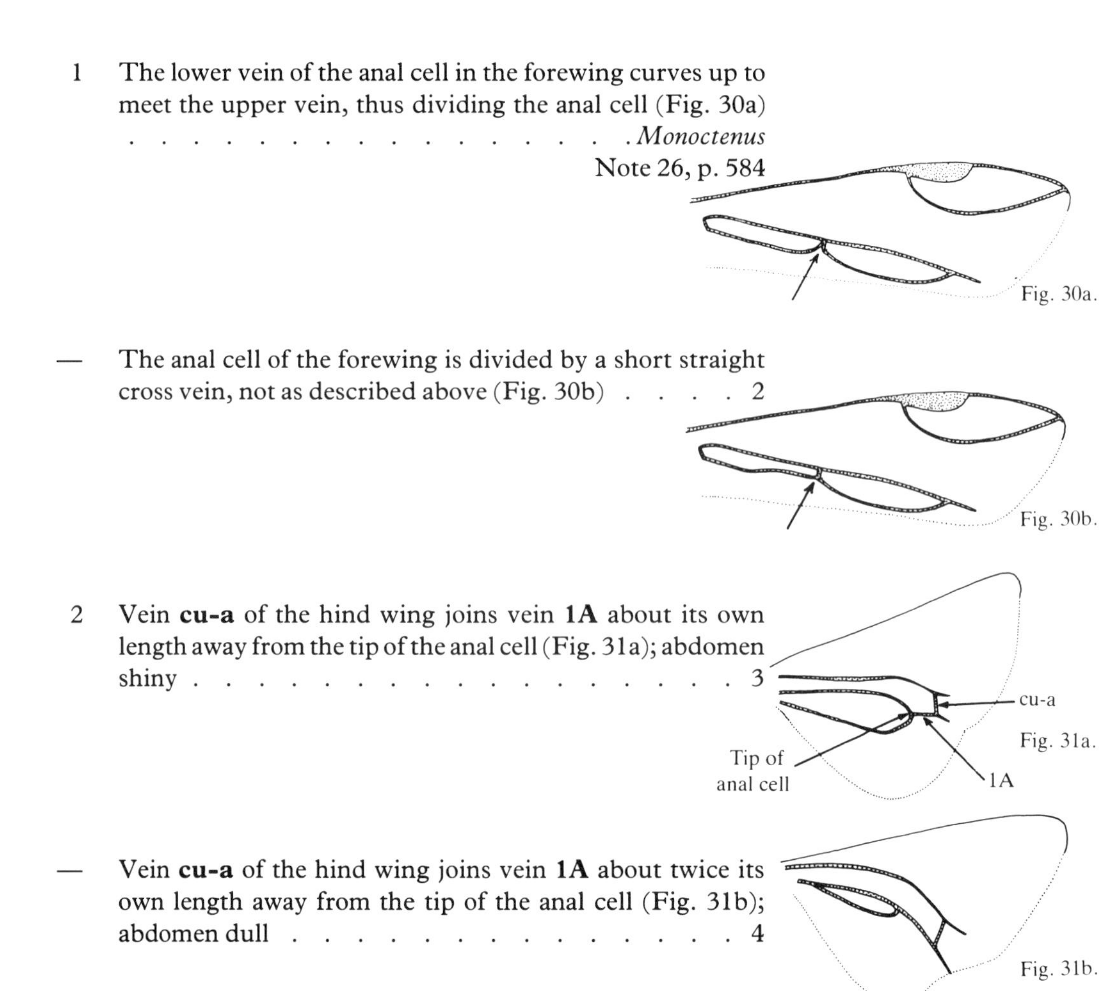

Fig. 30a.

Fig. 30b.

Fig. 31a.

Fig. 31b.

3 Hind tarsal claws with an inner tooth (Fig. 32a) *Neodiprion*
Note 28, p. 584

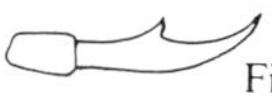

Fig. 32a.

— Hind tarsal claws lacking an inner tooth (Fig. 32b) . . .
Microdiprion
Note 27, p. 584

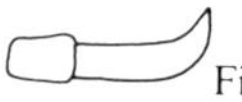

Fig. 32b.

4 Distance between the cenchri at least 1.5 times the length of one cenchrus (as seen from above) (Fig. 33a) . . *Diprion*
Note 29, p. 584

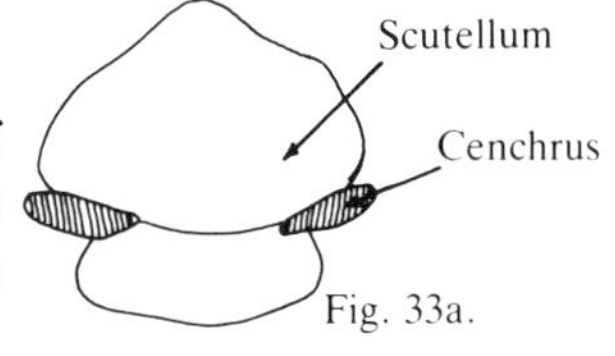

Fig. 33a.

— Distance between the cenchri equal to or less than the length of one cenchrus (as seen from above) (Fig. 33b) . .
Gilpinia
Note 30, p. 584

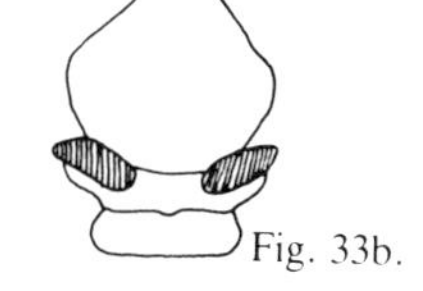
Fig. 33b.

KEY 8

A KEY TO THE SUBFAMILIES OF THE FAMILY TENTHREDINIDAE

- Size variable, from 2.0–15 mm
- Antennae usually 9-segmented, but may be 10–15 segmented
- Largest sawfly family in the world, containing 80% of the British sawfly fauna

Note: The illustrations given here show only the part of the wing venation which is useful for identification purposes. 'Real' specimens will have more complex venation.

1 Vein **2R** absent from the forewing (Fig. 34a) OR wings not reaching the end of the abdomen . . . . **Nematinae**
KEY 12, p. 572

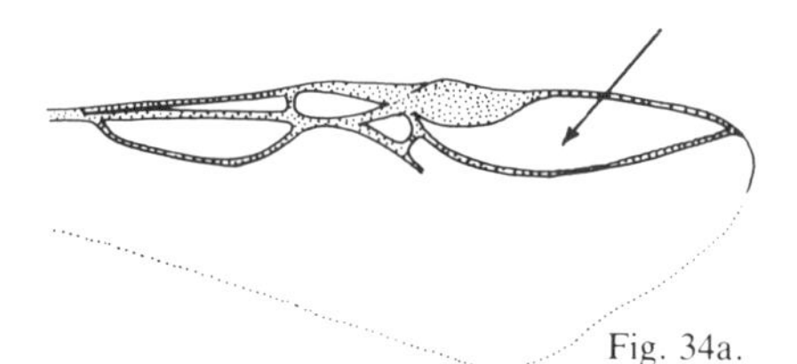

Fig. 34a.

— Vein **2R** present in the forewing (Fig. 34b) even if as a faint shadow; wings reach to, or beyond, the end of the abdomen 2

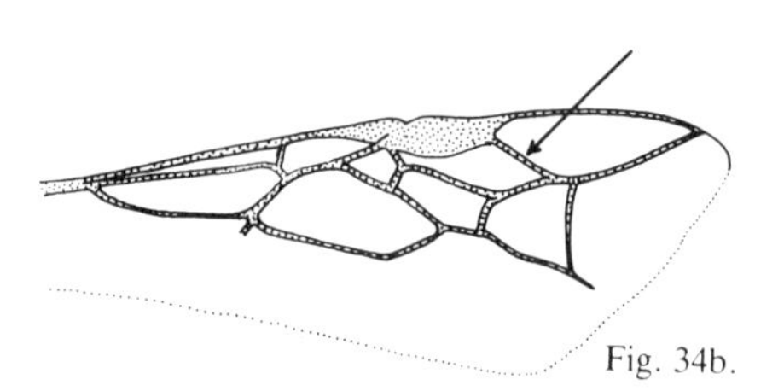

Fig. 34b.

2 Anal cell of the forewing as illustrated, either with (Fig. 35a) or without (Fig. 35b) an oblique cross vein 3

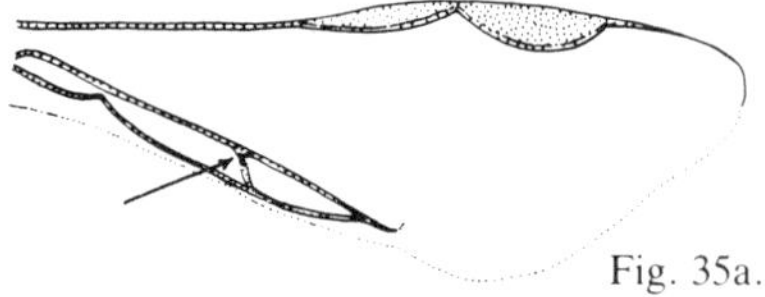

Fig. 35a.

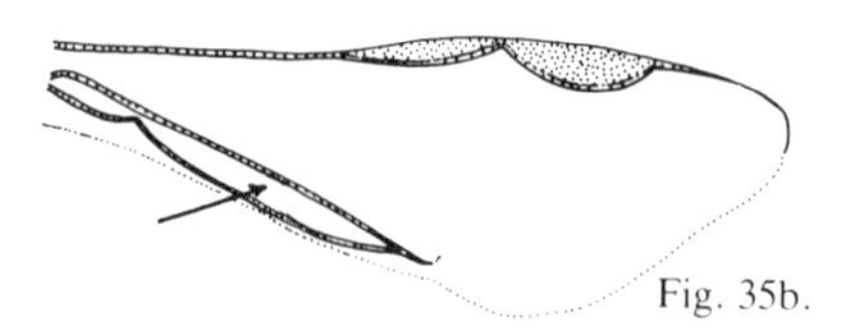

Fig. 35b.

— Anal cell of the forewing of different shape, for example greatly constricted in the middle (Fig. 35c) or petiolate (stalked) (Fig. 35d) 5

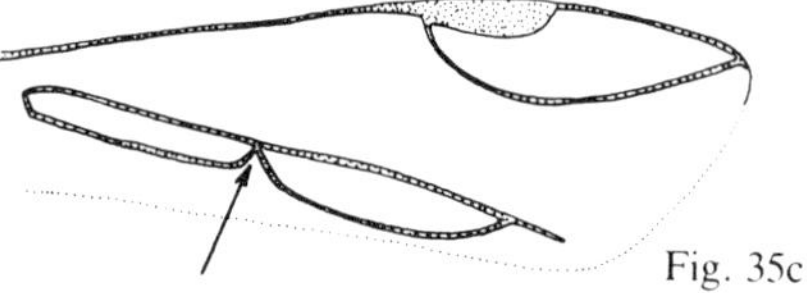

Fig. 35c.

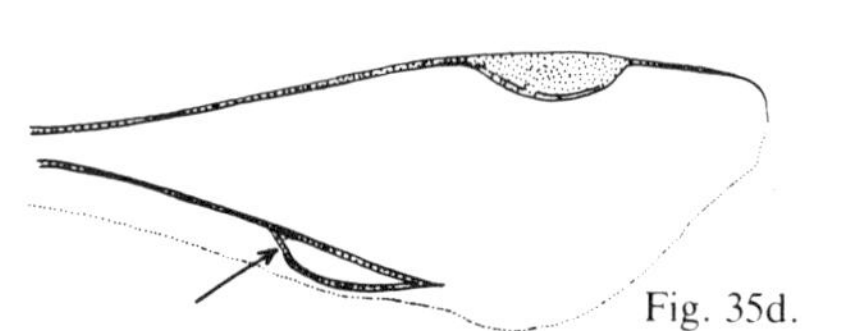

Fig. 35d.

3 Base of the vein **RS+M** in the forewing very strongly curved back towards the stigma (Fig. 36a) (be careful!); antennae always with 9 segments 4

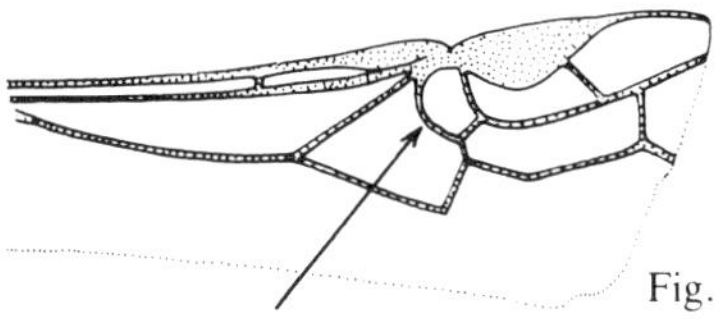

Fig. 36a.

— Base of the vein **RS+M** in the forewing not **strongly** recurved towards the stigma (Fig. 36b,c) (be careful!); antennae usually with 9 segments, but may have 10–15 segments 5

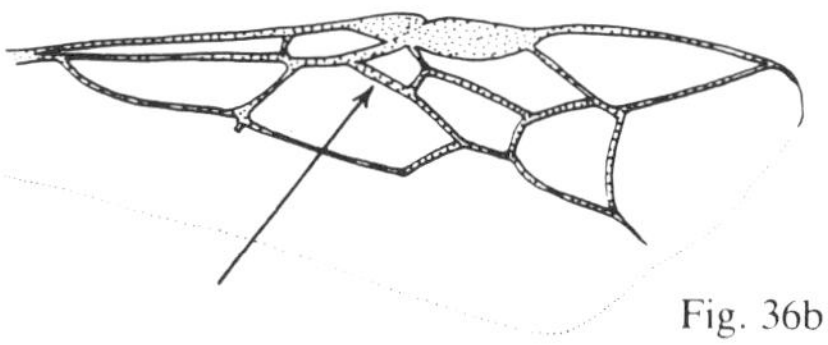

Fig. 36b.

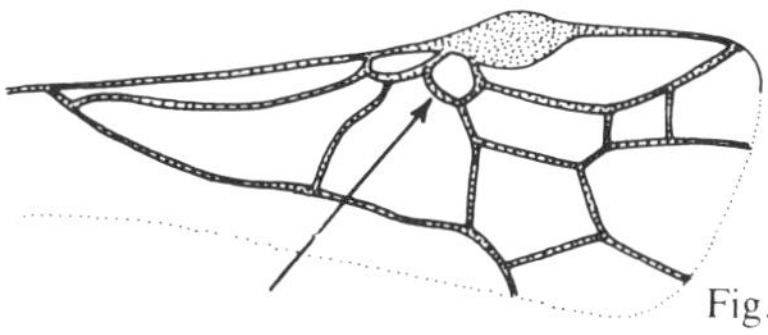

Fig. 36c.

4 Black insect, except for its rusty red mesonotum (see Fig. 2, p. 534) **Tenthredininae**
(Tribe Eriocampini)
KEY 11, p. 569

— Not coloured as above . . . . **Selandriinae**
KEY 9, p. 557

5 Subcostal vein of the forewing dips strongly where it is joined by vein **M** (Fig. 37a) 6

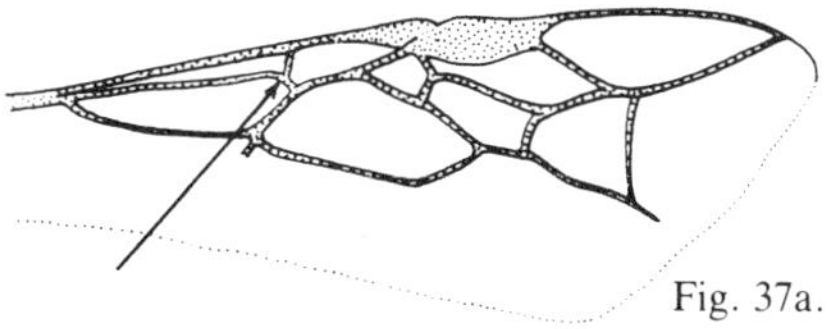

Fig. 37a.

— Subcostal vein of the forewing not dipped as above (Fig. 37b) 7

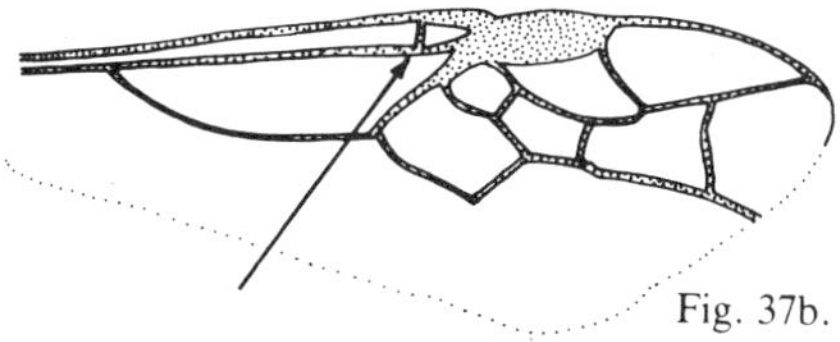

Fig. 37b.

6 Intercostal vein present in the forewing; insects 6.0–14.0 mm long (Fig. 38a) . . . **Tenthredininae**
KEY 11, p. 569

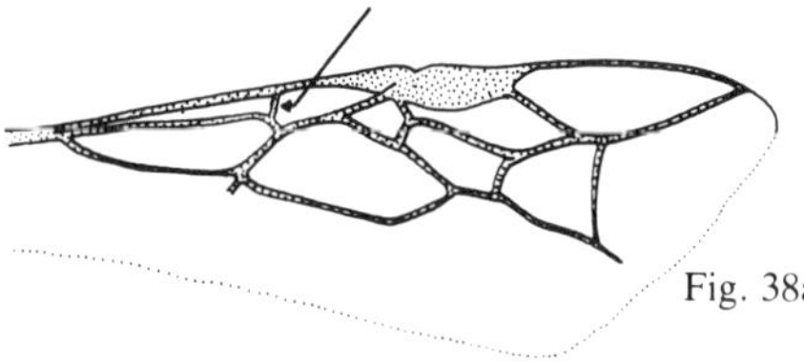

Fig. 38a.

— Intercostal vein absent from the forewing (Fig. 38b); insects 2.0–5.0 mm long . . **Blennocampinae**
(Tribe Fenusini)
KEY 10, p. 560

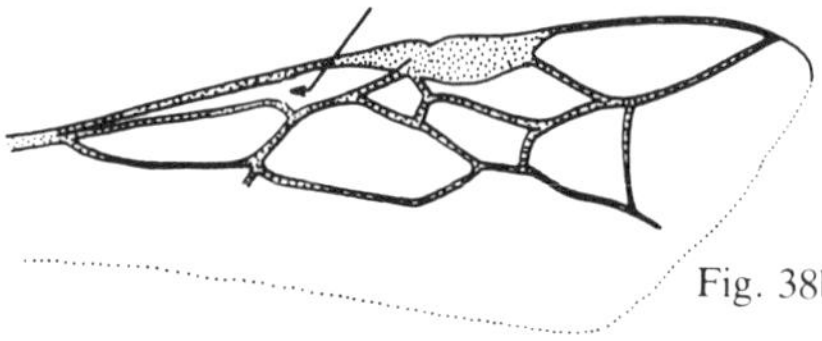

Fig. 38b.

7 Anal cell of the forewing completely enclosed and with an oblique cross vein (Fig. 39) 8

— Anal cell of the forewing of different shape 11

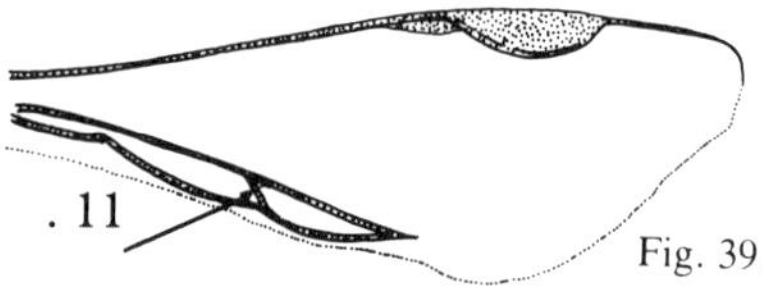

Fig. 39.

8 Hindwing with a marginal vein and/or an enclosed middle cell (Fig. 40 a,b) . . . **Blennocampinae**
(Tribes Athalini, Allantini, Empriini & Caliroini)
KEY 10, p. 560

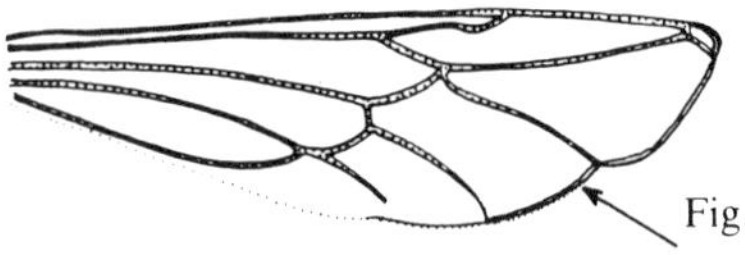

Fig. 40a.

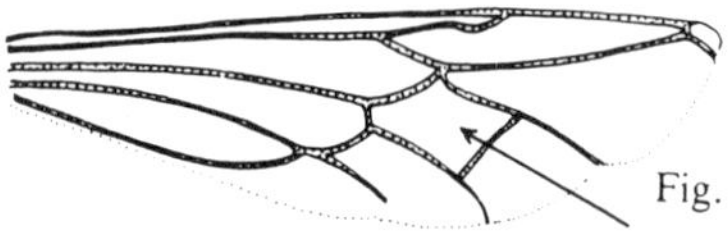

Fig. 40b.

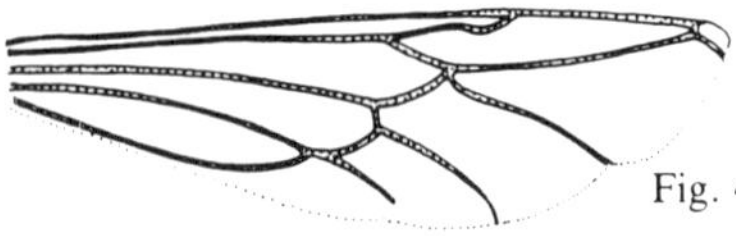

Fig. 40c.

— Hindwing lacking both a marginal vein and an enclosed middle cell (Fig. 40c) . 9

9 Anal cell of the hindwing is short and poorly defined (Fig. 41a) . **Heterarthrinae**
(One genus, *Heterarthrus*, Note 43, p. 585)

HETERARTHRINAE CHECK CHARACTERS

- Size variable, from 4.0–5.5 mm
- Antennae 10–15 segmented
- Larvae mine leaves of various trees

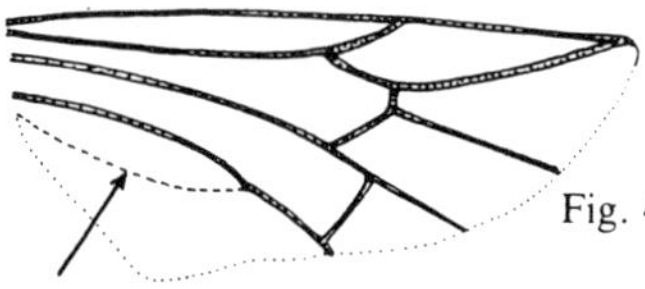

Fig. 41a.

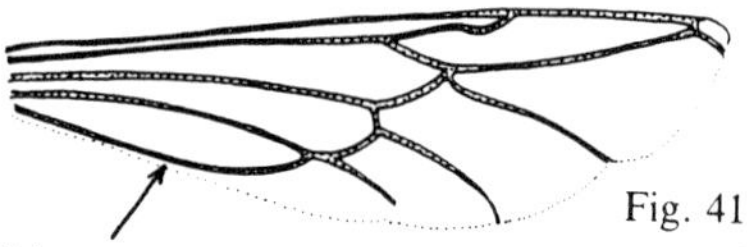

Fig. 41b.

— Anal cell of the hindwing clearly defined (Fig. 41b) 10

10 Vein **cu-a** of the hindwing shorter than its distance away from the tip of the anal cell (Fig. 42a) . . . . **Heterarthrinae**
(One genus, *Heterarthrus*, see check characters above; Note 43, p. 585)

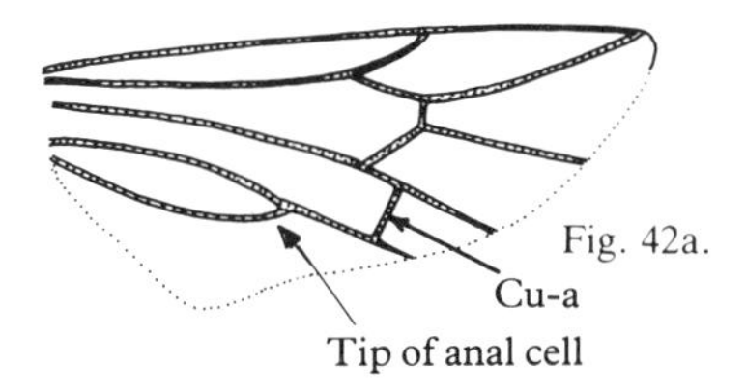

Fig. 42a.

— Vein **cu-a** of the hindwing longer than its distance away from the tip of the anal cell (Fig. 42b,c) . . . . **Blennocampinae**
(Tribes Athalini, Allantini, Empriini & Caliroini)
KEY 10, p. 560

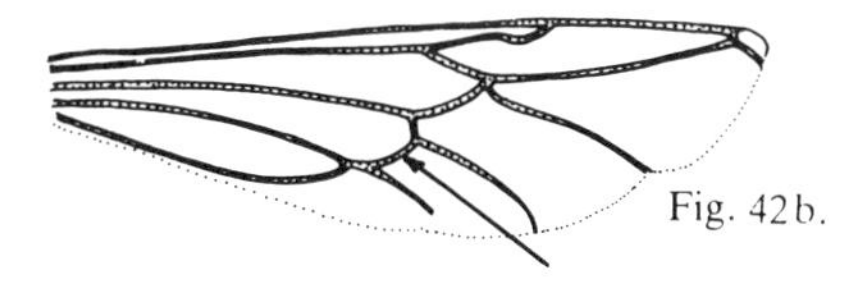
Fig. 42b.

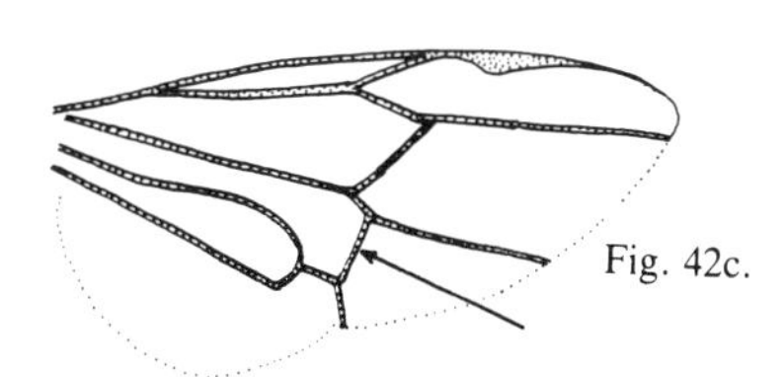
Fig. 42c.

11 Veins **1mcu** and **2mcu** of the forewing clearly enter cell **1RS** (Fig. 43a) **Nematinae**
KEY 12, p. 572

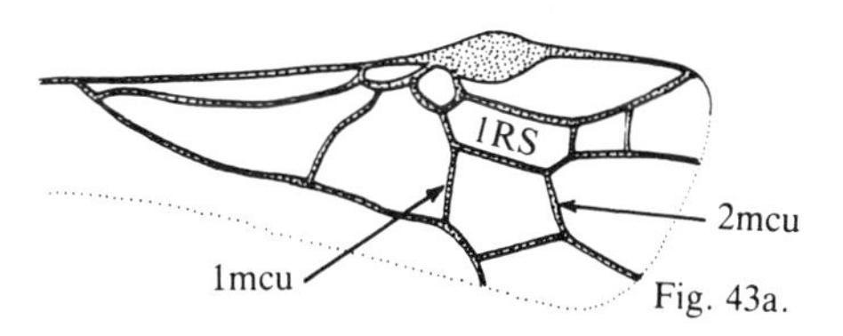

Fig. 43a.

— Veins **1mcu** and **2mcu** of the forewing enter different cells (e.g. Fig. 43b), or vein **2mcu** touches the junction of **1RS** and **2RS** (Fig. 43c) 12

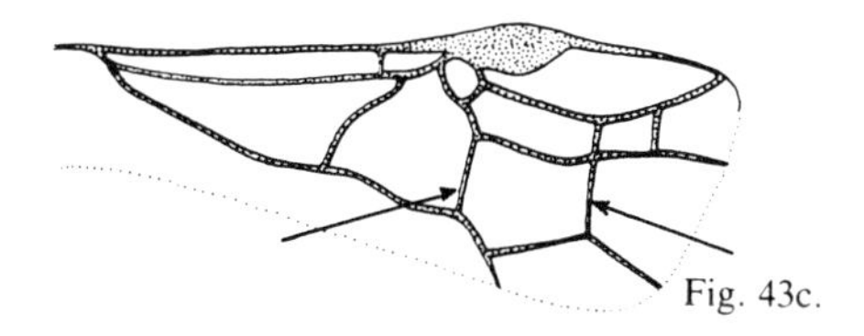
Fig. 43c.

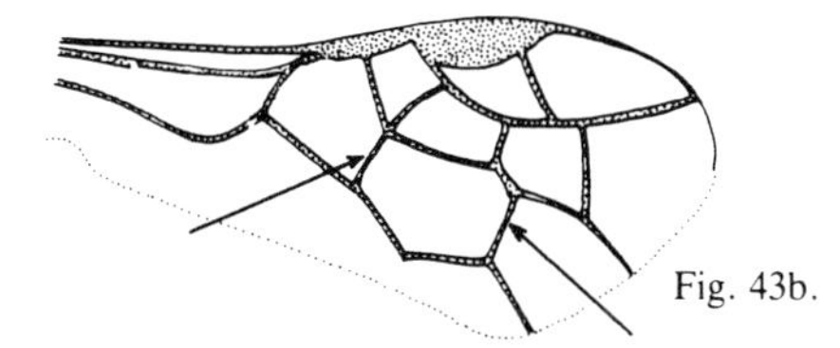
Fig. 43b.

12 Hindwing with two enclosed middle cells (Fig. 44a) . . . . **Nematinae**
(genera *Endophytus* & *Hoplocampa*)
KEY 12, p. 572

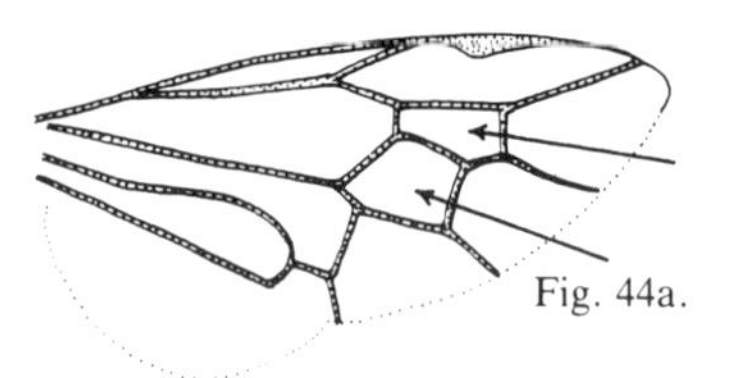
Fig. 44a.

— Hindwing with 1 or no enclosed middle cells (Fig. 44b,c) . . . .
Blennocampinae
(Tribes Blennocampini and Fenusini)
KEY 10, p. 560

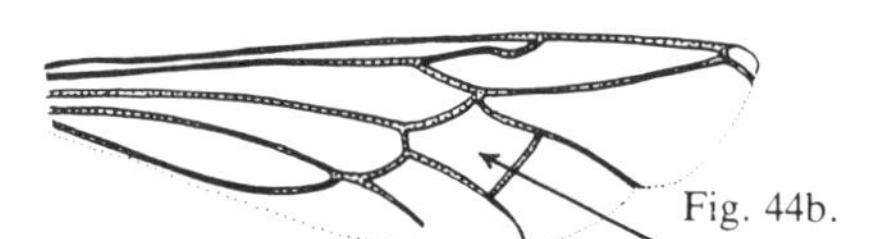
Fig. 44b.

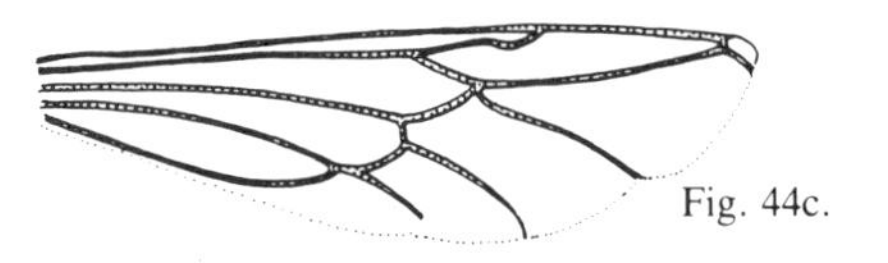
Fig. 44c.

KEY 9

Key to the British Genera of the Sub-Family Selandriinae (FAMILY TENTHREDINIDAE)

- Usually 5.0–14 mm long
- Antennae 9-segmented
- Vein RS + M of forewing strongly recurved towards stigma

Note: The illustrations given here show only the part of the wing venation which is useful for identification purposes. Real specimens will have more complex venation.

1 Vein **2RM** absent from the forewing (Fig. 45a) . . . 2

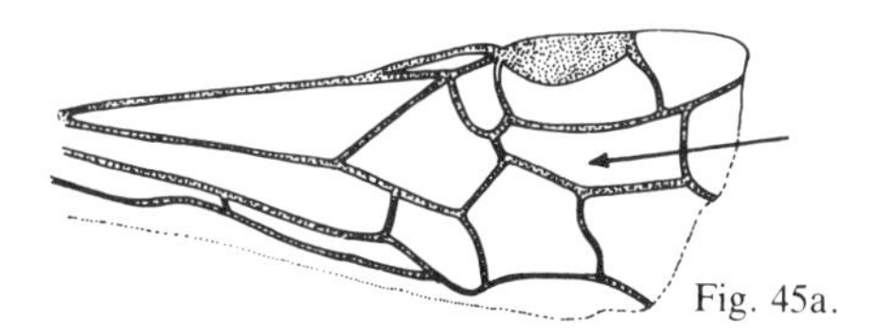

Fig. 45a.

— Vein **2RM** present in forewing (Fig. 45b,c) though it may sometimes be faint. . 3

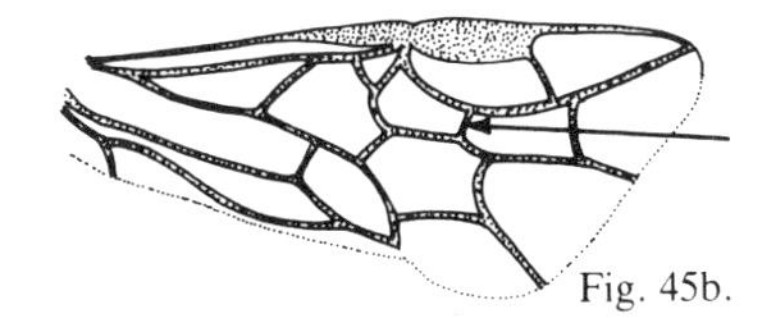

Fig. 45b.

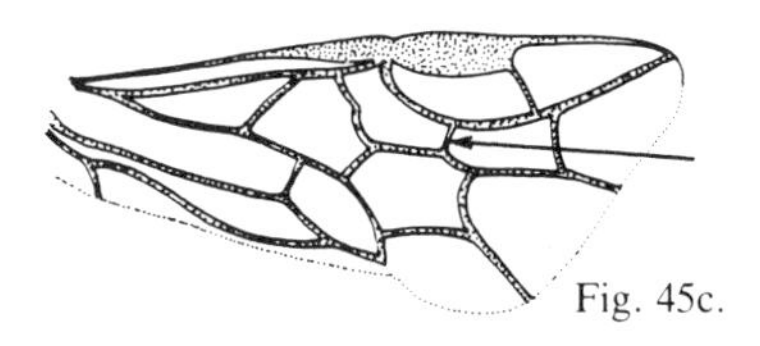

Fig. 45c.

2 Inner eye margin convex or flat (Fig. 46a) (view head from in front); tegulae black or red, but never marked with white . . . . *Dolerus*
Notes 40 & 42, p. 585

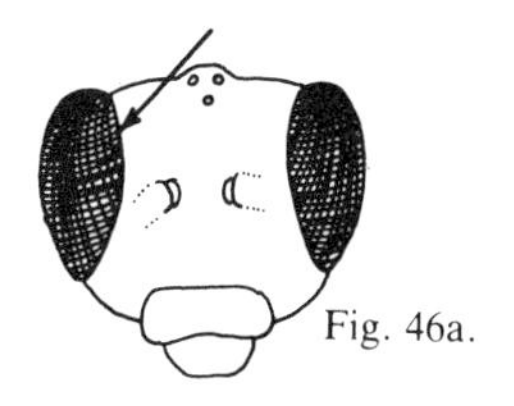

Fig. 46a.

— Inner eye margin concave, eyes elongate (Fig. 46b); tegulae usually black with white markings . . . . . . *Loderus*
Notes 40 & 41, p. 585

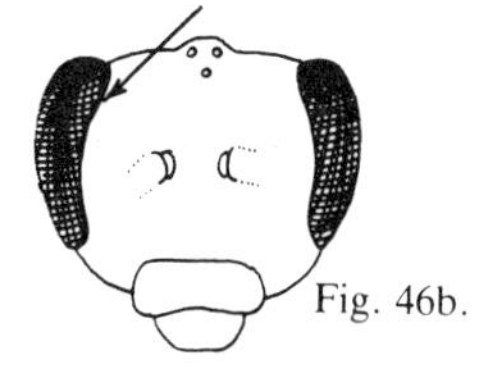

Fig. 46b.

3 Veins **m** and **cu-a** of the forewing touch (Fig. 47a) OR very nearly touch (at most only a vein's width apart) (Fig. 47b). *Heptamelus*
Note 32, p. 584

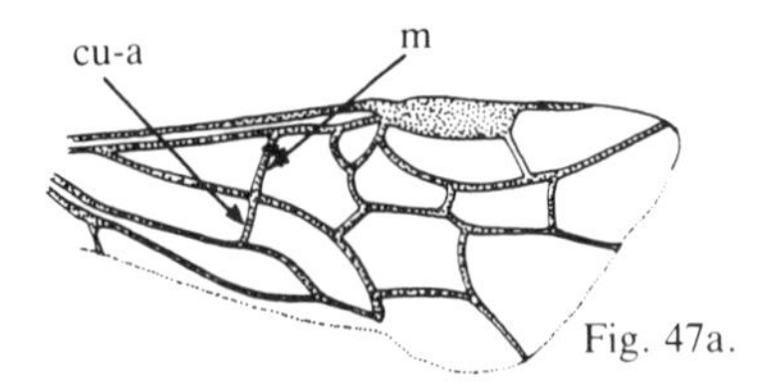

Fig. 47a.

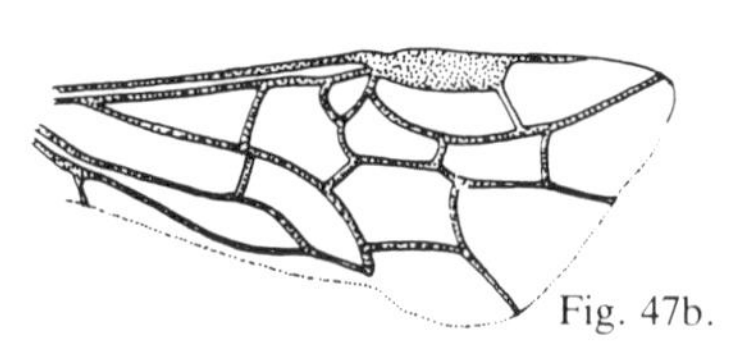
Fig. 47b.

— Veins **m** and **cu-a** of the forewing clearly do not touch (Fig. 47c) 4

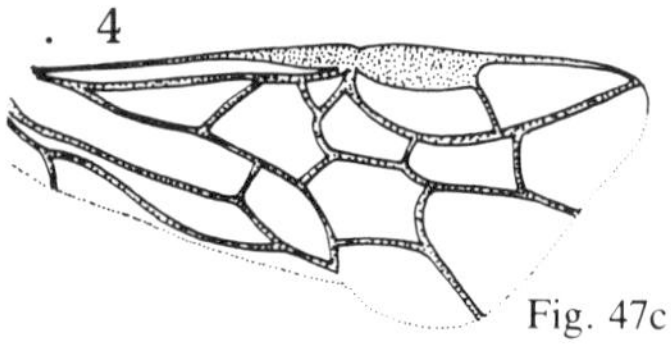

Fig. 47c.

4 Scutellum pale (see Fig. 2e, p. 534) . . . . *Strombocerus*
Note 34, p. 584

— Scutellum black (see Fig. 2e, p. 534) 5

5 Anal cell of the forewing with a cross vein (Fig. 48a). . . . *Pseudohemitaxonus*
Note 33, p. 584

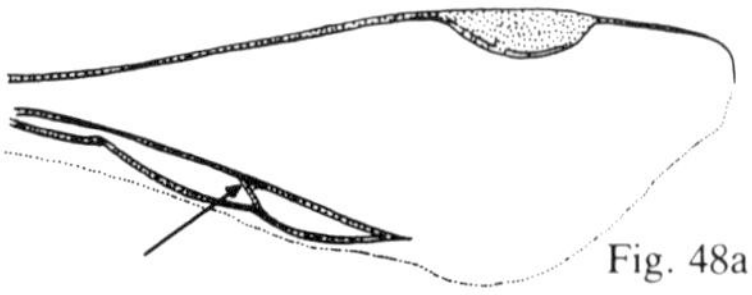

Fig. 48a.

Fig. 48b.

— Anal cell of the forewing lacks a cross vein (Fig. 48b) . 6

6 Tegulae black 7

— Tegulae pale or pale marked 8

7 Hind femora black. . . . . *Birka*
Note 31 & 37, p. 584

— Hind femora pale . . . . *Nesoselandria*
Note 31 & 37, p. 584

8 Cell **RS** of the hind wing touches cell **C** (Fig. 49a,b) . 9

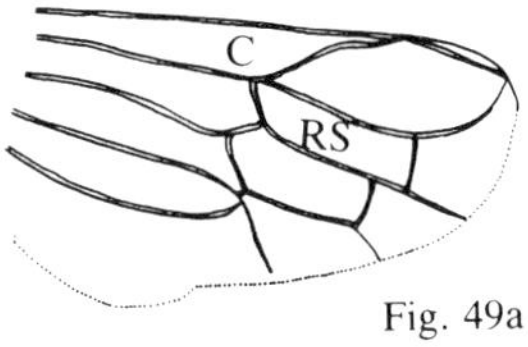

Fig. 49a.

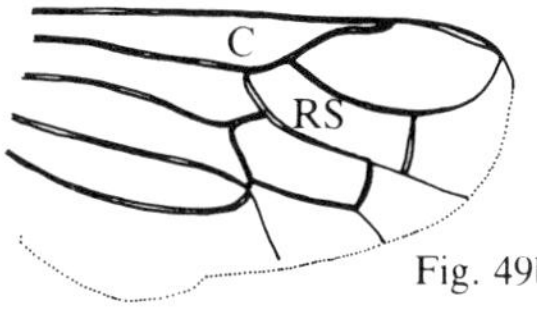

Fig. 49b.

— Cell **RS** of the hind wing does not touch cell **C** (Fig. 49c) 10

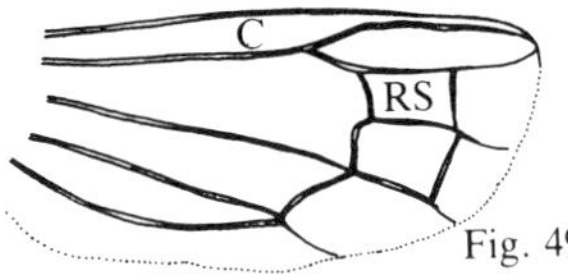

Fig. 49c.

9 1st tarsal segment of the hind leg as long as, or nearly as long as, the following 3 segments together (Fig. 50a) *Selandria*
Note 39, p. 585

Fig. 50a.

— 1st tarsal segment of the hind leg definitely shorter than the next three segments together (Fig. 50b) . . *Brachythops*
Note 38, p. 585

Fig. 50b.

10 Abdomen either completely black or completely brown . *Aneugmenus*
Note 36, p. 584

— Abdomen black and orange, or dark with cream bands . . *Strongylogaster*
Note 35, p. 584

KEY 10

KEY TO THE BRITISH GENERA OF THE SUB-FAMILY BLENNOCAMPINAE (FAMILY TENTHREDINIDAE)

- Usually 2.0–10.0 mm long
- Antennae usually 9-segmented, but may be 10–11 segmented
- Large and variable group, containing about 100 British species

1 Anal cell of the forewing with an oblique cross-vein . . 2

Note: All species keying through this lead belong to the tribes Athalini, Allantini, Empriini and Caliroini

— Anal cell of the forewing without a cross-vein 18

Note: All species keying through the second lead here belong to the tribes Blennocampini and Fenusini

2 Inner spur of front tibia simple (Fig. 51a); orange and black insect . . . . *Athalia*
Note 44, p. 585

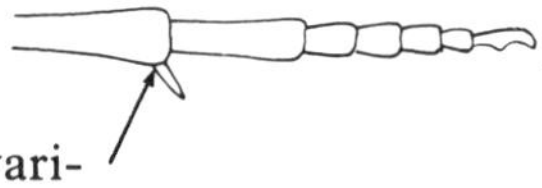

Fig. 51a.

— Inner spur of front tibia distinctly forked (Fig. 51b); various colours 3

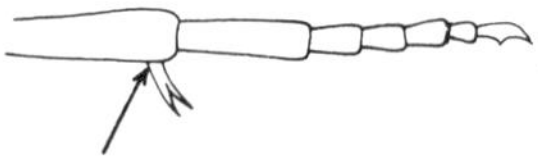

Fig. 51b.

3 Insect black, with paired white or grey spots on at least three abdominal tergites (Fig. 52). . . . . . *Empria*
Note 48, p. 586

Fig. 52

— Abdominal colouration not like this 4

4 Green and black sawfly, with green or white stigma; tiny, up to 5 mm long . . . . *Harpiphorus*
Note 45, p. 585

— Species differently coloured; stigma colouration ranges from pale brown to black, but is never green or white; insects of various sizes 5

5 Abdomen and tegulae are both entirely black 6

— Abdomen and/or the tegulae are not entirely black . . 10

6 Vein **RS** present in the forewing (Fig. 53a), or at least indicated by a 'shadow' 7

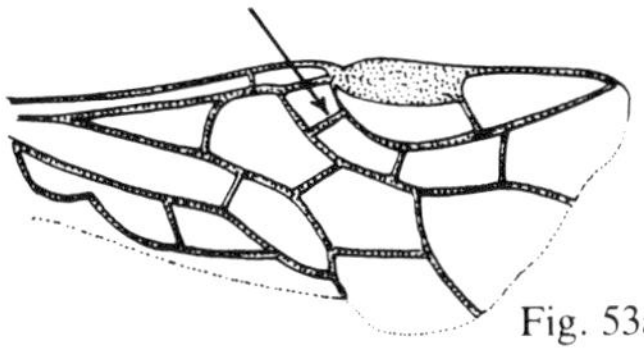

Fig. 53a.

— Forewing without any trace of vein **RS** (Fig. 53b) . . 9

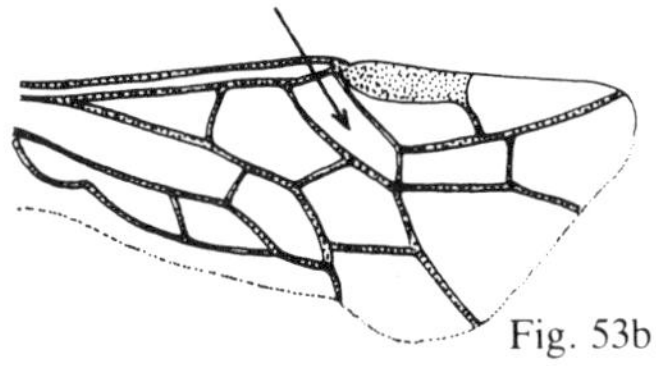

Fig. 53b.

7 Clypeus deeply emarginate (Fig. 54a) (view from in front of the head) . . . . *Ametastegia*
Note 49, p. 586

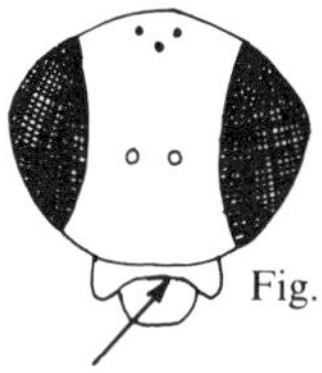

Fig. 54a.

Fig. 54b.

— Clypeus not as above (Fig. 54b) (view from in front of the head) 8

8 Lower vein of the anal cell in the forewing is smoothly curved (Fig. 55a) . . . . *Caliroa*
Notes 53 & 54, p. 586

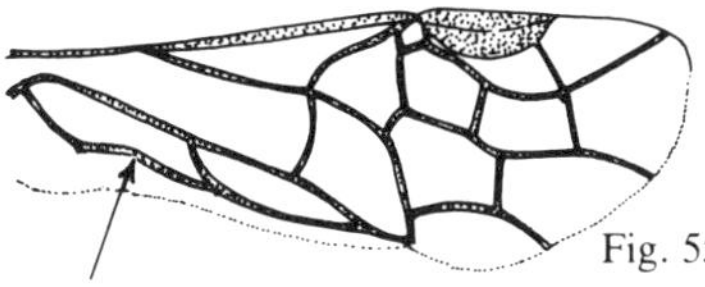

Fig. 55a.

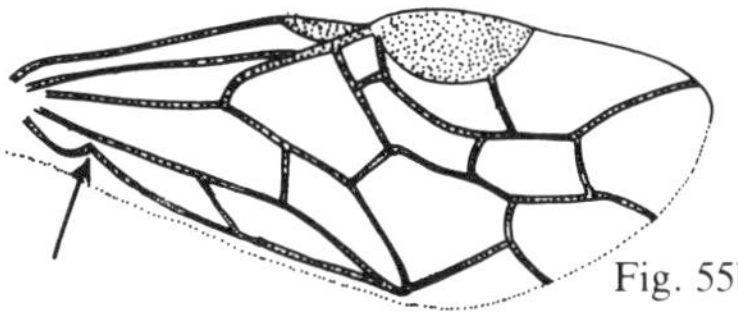

Fig. 55b.

— Lower vein of the anal cell in the forewing with a sharp kink (Fig. 55b) . . . . *Endelomyia*
Note 53, p. 586

9 Labrum white, or hind femora orange . . . . . *Allantus*
Note 51, p. 586

— Labrum black and hind femora dark brown/black . . . *Protoemphytus*
Note 49, p. 586

10 Hind wing with 2 enclosed middle cells (Fig. 56a) . . . *Taxonus* (female)
Note 49, p. 586

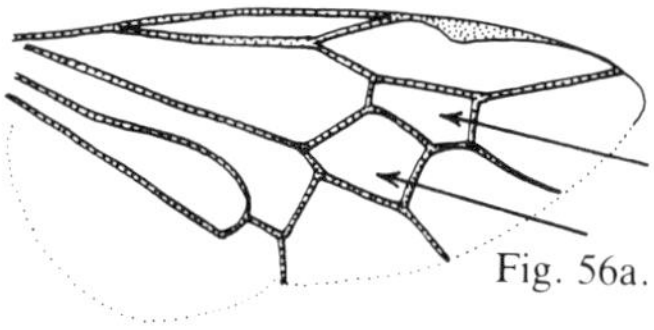

Fig. 56a.

— Hind wing with one or no enclosed middle cells (Fig. 56 b,c) 11

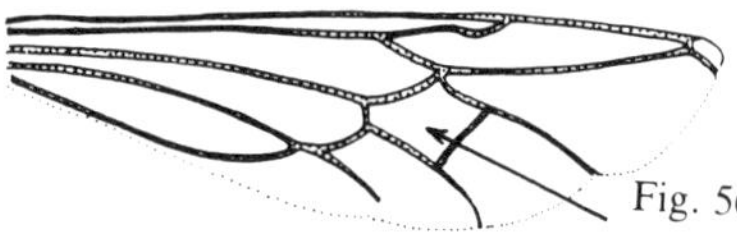

Fig. 56b.

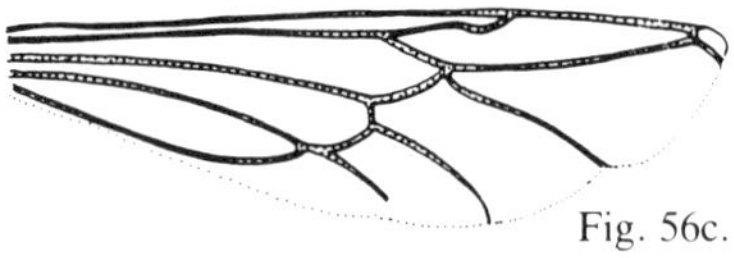

Fig. 56c.

11 Hind wing with 1 enclosed middle cell (Fig. 57a). . . . 12

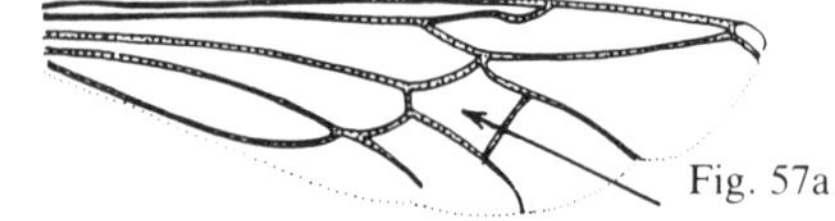

Fig. 57a.

— Hind wing without an enclosed middle cell (Fig. 57b) . 13

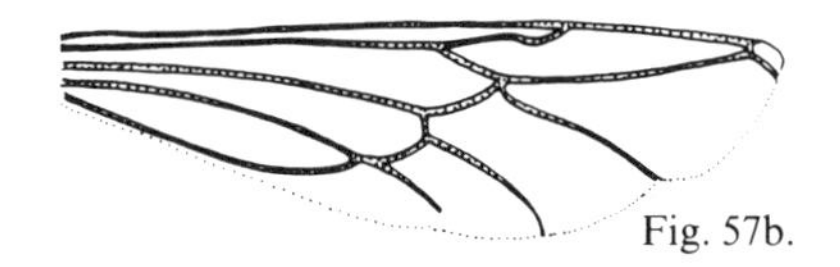

Fig. 57b.

12 Abdomen predominantly orange . . . . . . *Monostegia*
Note 46, p. 585

— Abdomen black with a pale margin to each segment . . . *Monosoma*
Note 47, p. 585

13 Vein **RS** present in the forewing (Fig. 58a). 14

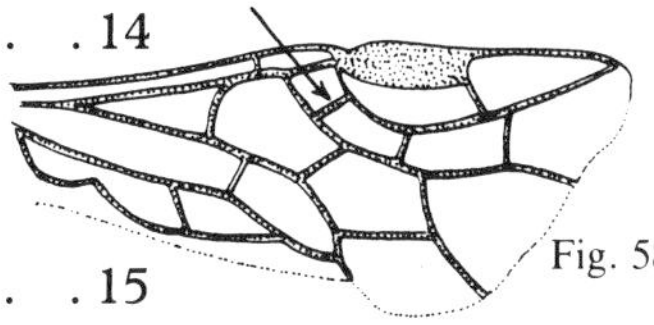

— Forewing without vein **RS** (Fig. 58b) 15

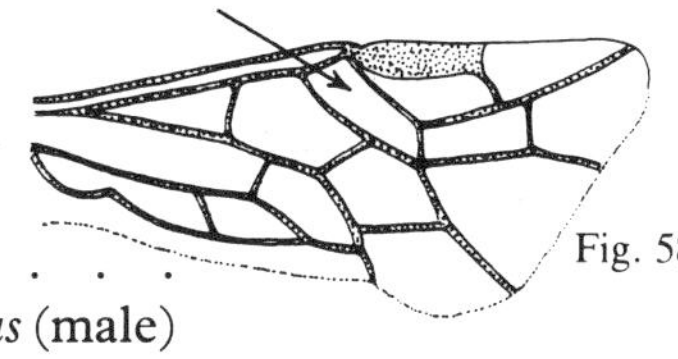

Fig. 58a.

Fig. 58b.

14 Marginal vein present in the hind wing (Fig. 59a) . . . *Taxonus* (male)
Note 49, p. 586

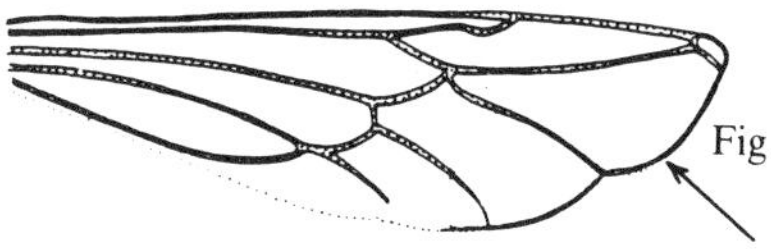

Fig. 59a.

— Marginal vein absent from the hind wing (Fig. 59b). . . *Ametastegia*
Note 49, p. 586

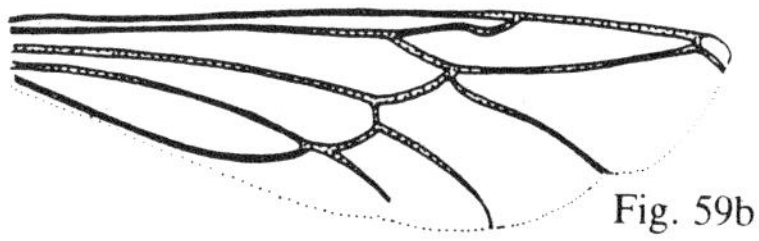

Fig. 59b.

15 Antennae very long: 8th segment four times as long as broad (Fig. 60a) . . . . *Apethymus*
Note 52, p. 586

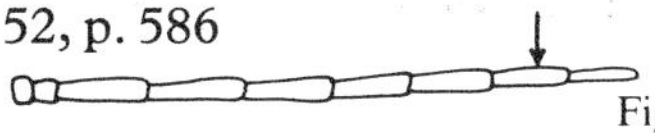

Fig. 60a.

— Antenna short: 8th segment two or three times as long as broad (Fig. 60b) 16

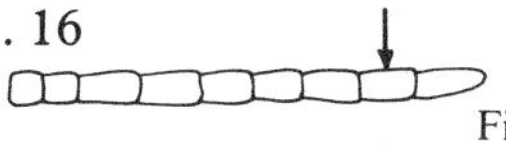

Fig. 60b.

16 Abdomen with a red, yellow or white girdle . . *Allantus*
Note 51, p. 586

— Abdomen entirely black or brown. 17

17 Tegulae entirely white; pronotum entirely black . . *Protoemphytus* Note 49, p. 586

— Colouration other than above; if the tegulae are entirely white, then the pronotum is also edged with white . . . . *Allantus* Note 51, p. 586

18 Vein **A3** of the forewing forked (Fig. 61a) . . . 19

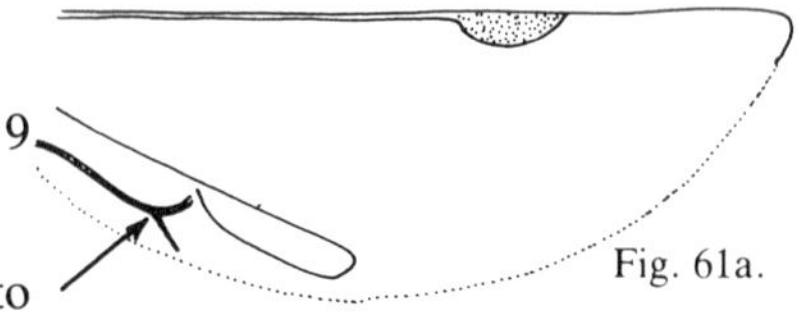

Fig. 61a.

— Vein **A3** of the forewing not forked (take care not to confuse the anal wing fold with part of vein A3) (Fig. 61b,c) 21

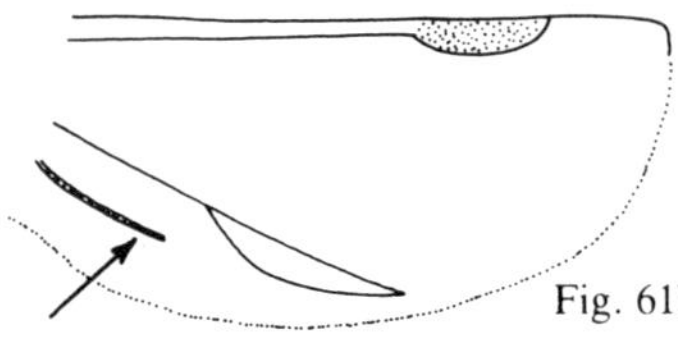

Fig. 61b.

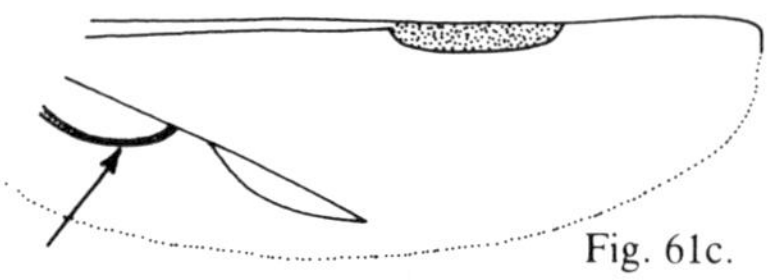

Fig. 61c.

19 Labrum yellowish white; tibiae of the legs dark brown *Dicrostema* Note 56, p. 586

— Labrum black; legs black. 20

20 8th antennal segment roughly 5 times as long as broad *Phymatocera* Note 55, p. 586

— 8th antennal segment about 2.5 times as long as broad *Rhadinoceraea* Note 56, p. 586

21 Hind margin of the eye with a series of deep pits (Fig.62) . . . . *Ardis* Note 60, p. 587

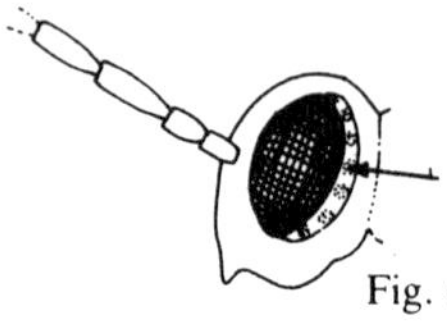

Fig. 62

— Hind margin of the eye normal, without a series of deep pits, although slight indentations may be present 22

22 Vein **A3** of the forewing bends back towards vein **A1** (Fig. 63a) 23

— Vein **A3** of the forewing straight (Fig. 63b) 32

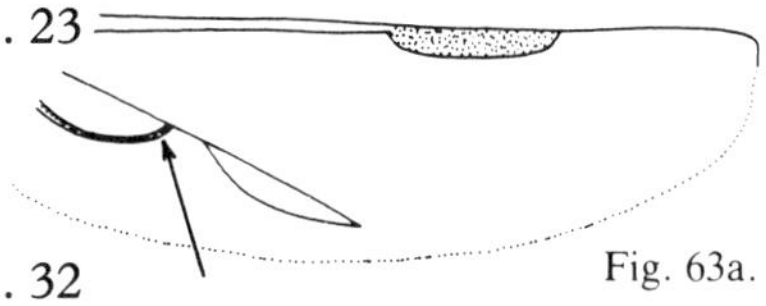

Fig. 63a.

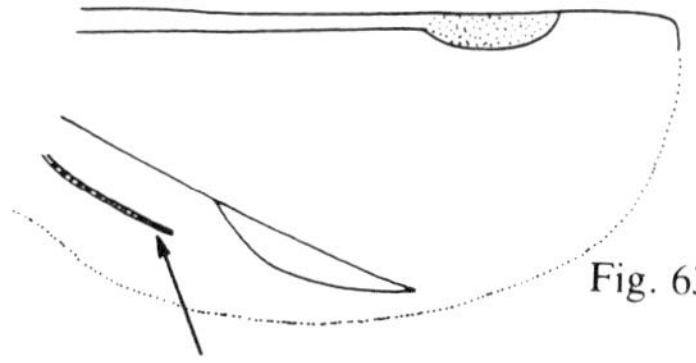

Fig. 63b.

23 Hind claws without a basal swelling (look carefully) (Fig. 64a,b) 24

— Hind claws have a basal swelling (Fig. 64c,d,e) . 28

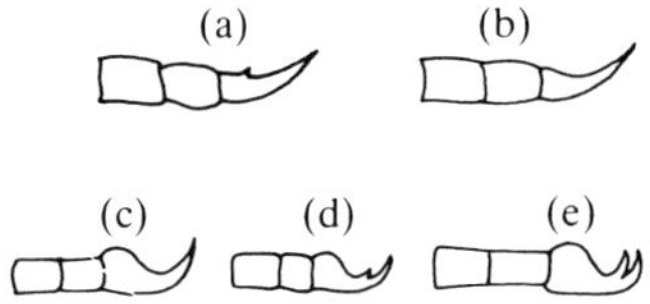

(a) (b) (c) (d) (e)

Fig. 64

24 Vein **2R** of the forewing meets cell **RS** before **2RM** does (Fig. 65a) 25

— Vein **2R** of the forewing meets cell **RS** after **2RM** does (Fig. 65b) 27

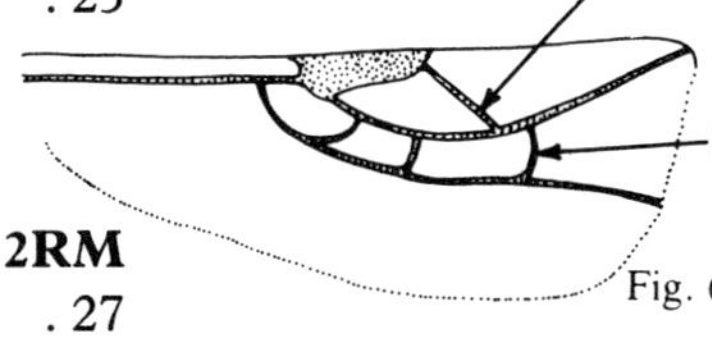

2R

2RM

Fig. 65a.

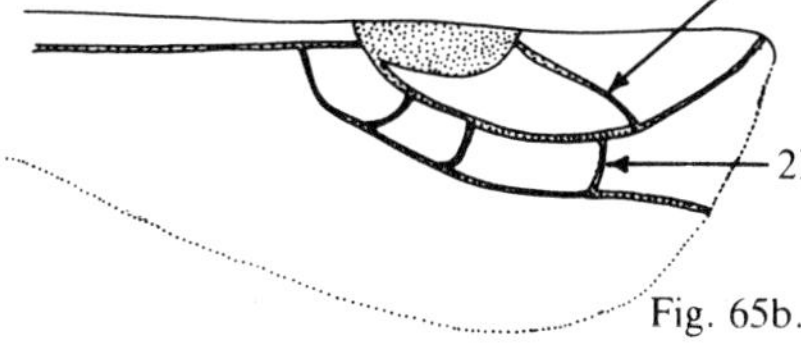

2R

2RM

Fig. 65b.

25 3rd antennal segment as long as the 3 apical segments together (Fig. 66a) . . . . *Tomostethus*
Note 56, p. 586

— 3rd antennal segment shorter than the combined length of the 3 apical segments (Fig. 66b) . . . 26

Fig. 66a.

Fig. 66b.

26 Abdomen mainly orange/yellow; hind femur dark . *Pareophora*
Note 61, p. 587

— Abdomen usually dark; but, if the abdomen is orange/yellow, then the hind femur is pale . *Eutomostethus*
Note 57, p. 586

27 4th tarsal segment of the hind legs extended below (Fig. 67a) . . . . *Fenusa*
Note 64, p. 587

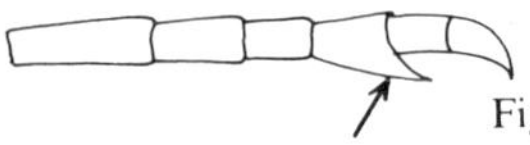

Fig. 67a.

— 4th tarsal segment of the hind legs normal (Fig. 67b) *Fenella*
Note 64, p. 587

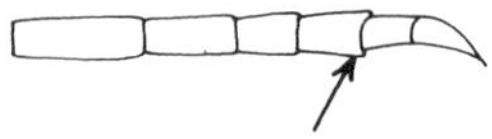

Fig. 67b.

28 Tarsal claws without inner teeth (Fig. 68a) 29

Fig. 68a.

— Tarsal claws with inner teeth (Fig. 68b,c) 30

Fig. 68b.

Fig. 68c.

29 Tegulae black . . . . *Scolioneura*
Note 63, p. 587

— Tegulae pale or pale marked . . . . . . *Messa*
Note 64, p. 587

30 3rd antennal segment at least as long as the 3 apical segments together (Fig. 69a) . . . . *Halidamia*
Note 61, p. 587

Fig. 69a.

— 3rd antennal segment not as long as the 3 apical segments together (Fig. 69b) 31

Fig. 69b.

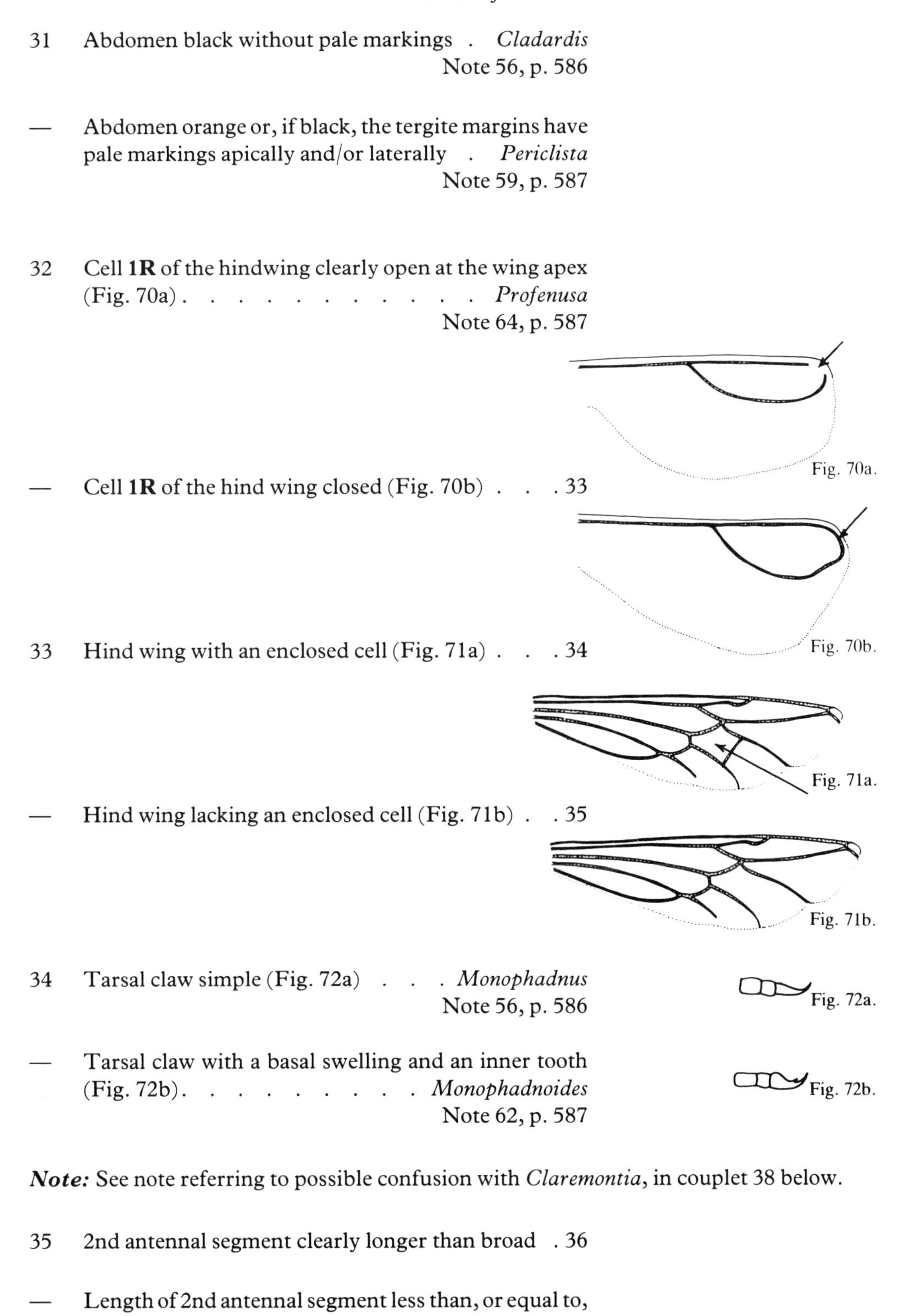

31 Abdomen black without pale markings . *Cladardis*
Note 56, p. 586

— Abdomen orange or, if black, the tergite margins have pale markings apically and/or laterally . *Periclista*
Note 59, p. 587

32 Cell **1R** of the hindwing clearly open at the wing apex (Fig. 70a) . . . . *Profenusa*
Note 64, p. 587

Fig. 70a.

— Cell **1R** of the hind wing closed (Fig. 70b) . . . 33

Fig. 70b.

33 Hind wing with an enclosed cell (Fig. 71a) . . . 34

Fig. 71a.

— Hind wing lacking an enclosed cell (Fig. 71b) . . 35

Fig. 71b.

34 Tarsal claw simple (Fig. 72a) . . . . *Monophadnus*
Note 56, p. 586

Fig. 72a.

— Tarsal claw with a basal swelling and an inner tooth (Fig. 72b). . . . . *Monophadnoides*
Note 62, p. 587

Fig. 72b.

Note: See note referring to possible confusion with *Claremontia*, in couplet 38 below.

35 2nd antennal segment clearly longer than broad . 36

— Length of 2nd antennal segment less than, or equal to, its breadth 38

36 Femur of the middle leg dark in contrast to the pale tibia . . . .
Blennocampa
Note 55, p. 586

— Femur and tibia of the middle leg both brown to black OR both pale (except perhaps at the extreme base of the femur) 37

37 Vein **cu-a** of the hind wing nearly twice its own length away from the apex of the anal cell (e.g. Fig. 73a) . . . . *Parna*
Note 63, p. 587

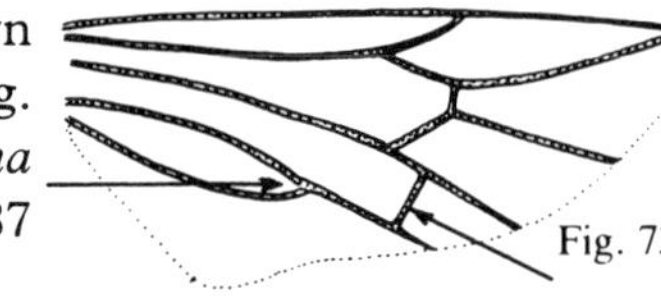

Fig. 73a.

— Vein **cu-a** of the hind wing scarcely its own length away from the apex of the anal cell (e.g. Fig. 73b) . .
Stethomostus
Note 58, p. 586

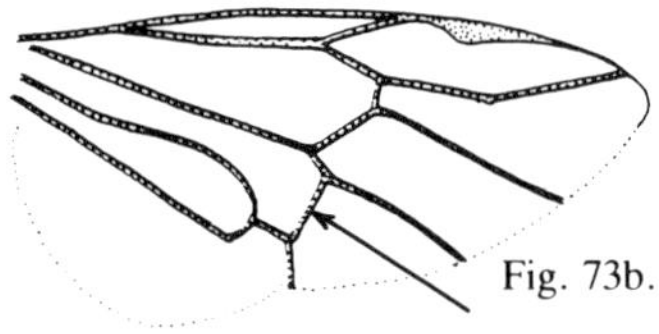

Fig. 73b.

38 Tarsal claws with an inner tooth (Fig. 74a) . . . .
Claremontia
Note 62, p. 587

Fig. 74a.

— Tarsal claws lacking an inner tooth (Fig. 74b) . . .
Metallus
Note 64, p. 587

Fig. 74b.

Note: Occasionally, some *Monophadnoides* spp. have aberrant venation and lack an enclosed cell in the hind wing. These will then key out to *Claremontia* spp. However, since the two genera were split after Benson's 1952 Royal Entomological Society key (see the bibliography), they will key out to species using that guide.

KEY 11

KEY TO THE BRITISH GENERA OF THE SUB-FAMILY TENTHREDININAE (FAMILY TENTHREDINIDAE)

- Usually 6.0–15.0 mm long; many species 10 mm or more
- Antennae 9-segmented
- Subcostal vein of forewing dips where it is joined by vein **M**

1 First abdominal tergite no split along the mid-line, but often with a raised median keel (carina) (Fig. 75a) . . . *Tenthredopis*
Note 67, p. 588

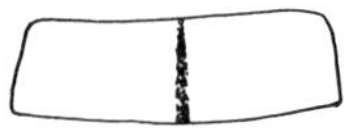

Fig. 75a.

— First abdominal tergite split along the mid-line (Fig. 75b) 2

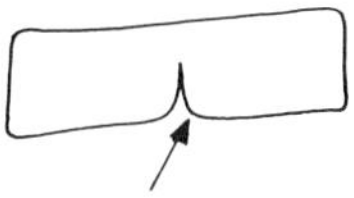

Fig. 75b.

2 Front angle of the scutellum acute (Fig. 76b) or only slightly obtuse (Fig. 76a), in which case the distance between the cenchri is less than or equal to the length of a single cenchrus 3

— Front angle of the scutellum clearly obtuse (Fig. 76c) or truncate (Fig. 76d) 4

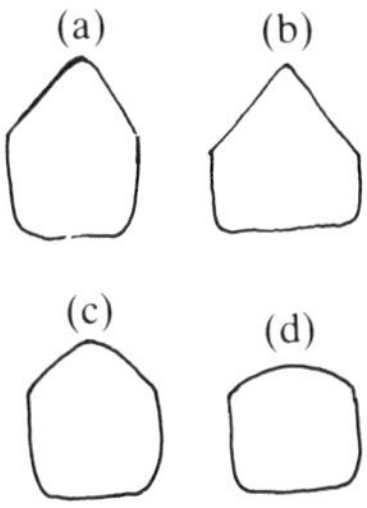

(a) (b) (c) (d)

Fig. 76.

3 Hind tarsal claws widely separated, the inner claw being very short (Fig. 77a) . . . . *Perineura*
Note 69, p. 588

Fig. 77a.

— Hind tarsal claws close together and of equal length (Fig. 77b) . . . . *Aglaostigma*
Note 66, p. 587

Fig. 77b.

4 Black insect, except for a rich chestnut colouration on top of the thorax . . . . *Eriocampa*
Note 65, p. 587

— Differently coloured insect 5

5 Carina (keel) missing from the upper hind margin of the head (if necessary, tilt the specimen to get a clear view of the head) (Fig. 78a); hind tibia with short and stout apical spurs (Fig. 78b) 6

Fig. 78a.

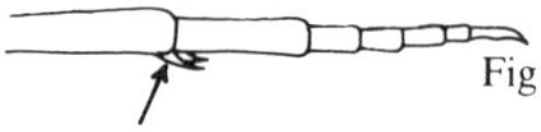

Fig. 78b.

— Carina fully developed around the hind margin of the head (Fig. 78c); hind tibia with long apical spurs (Fig. 78d) . 7

Fig. 78d.

Fig. 78c.

6 Eyes small, widely separated (Fig. 79a) (view from in front of the head) . . . . *Sciapteryx*
Note 68, p. 588

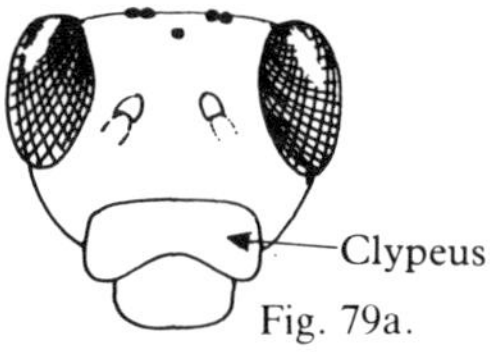

Fig. 79a.

— Eyes large, becoming closer together towards the clypeus (Fig. 79b) (view from in front of the head) . . . *Elinora*
Note 69, p. 588

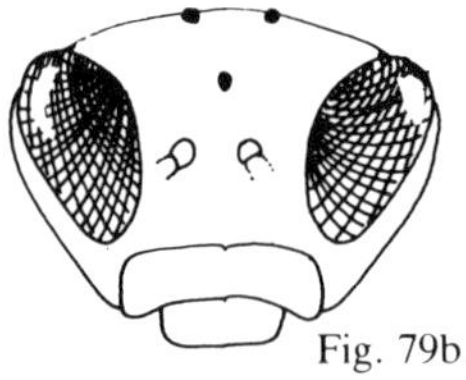

Fig. 79b.

7 Hind femur often extends beyond the tip of the abdomen, and is elongate (approximately as long as the hind tibia); labrum convex 8

— Hind femur shorter than the hind tibia, and does not extend beyond the tip of the abdomen; labrum flat 9

8 3rd and 4th antennal segments of almost equal length (Fig. 80a); antennae very long; eyes widely separated throughout . . . . *Pachyprotasis*
Note 72, p. 588

Fig. 80a.

— 3rd antennal segment at least 1.5 times as long as the 4th (Fig. 80b); eyes converging as they approach the clypeus . *Macrophya*
Notes 73 & 74, p. 588

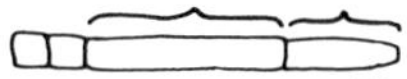

Fig. 80b.

9 Sawfly not green and black in colour . . . . *Tenthredo*
Note 71, p. 588

— Green and black sawfly 10

10 The eyes do not converge strongly, so that the distance between the eyes remains greater than the transverse length of the clypeus (Fig. 81a) . . . .*Rhogogaster*
Note 70, p. 588

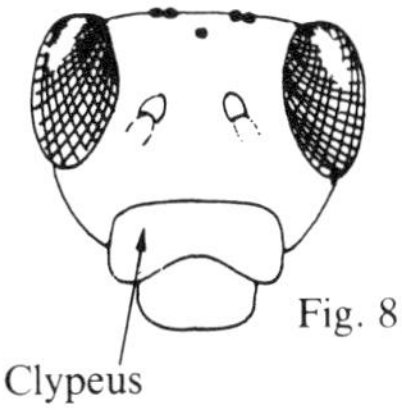

Clypeus

Fig. 81a.

— The eyes converge strongly as they approach the clypeus (so that the gap between the eyes becomes less than the transverse length of the clypeus (Fig. 81b) . . . . . .
Tenthredo
Note 71, p. 588

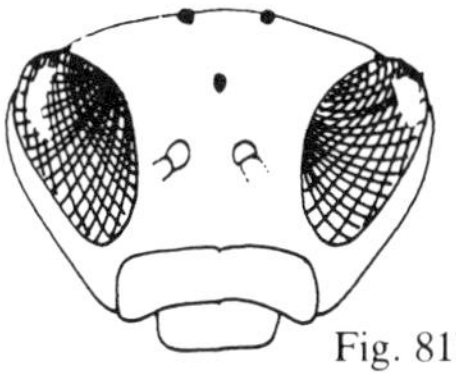

Fig. 81b.

KEY 12

KEY TO THE BRITISH GENERA OF THE SUB-FAMILY NEMATINAE (FAMILY TENTHREDINIDAE)

- Usually 4.0–12.0 mm long; most species under 10 mm
- Antennae 9-segmented
- Vein **2R** often absent in forewing
- Veins **1mcu** and **2mcu** of forewing often enter same cell
- Around 200 British species

Note: The illustrations given here show only the parts of the wing venation which are useful for identification. Real specimens will have more complex wing venation.

1 Tibiae and 1st tarsal segment of the hind leg greatly expanded and flattened (Fig. 82a) . . . . . . *Croesus*
Note 90, p. 590

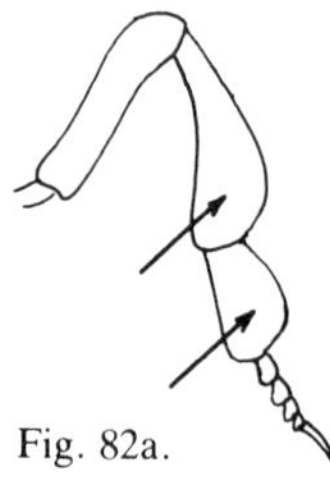
Fig. 82a.

— Tibiae and 1st tarsal segment of the hind leg not greatly expanded (Fig. 82b) 2

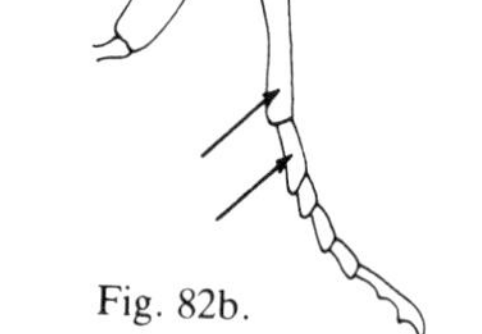
Fig. 82b.

2 Veins **1mcu** and **2mcu** of the forewing clearly enter different cells (Fig. 83a) . . 3

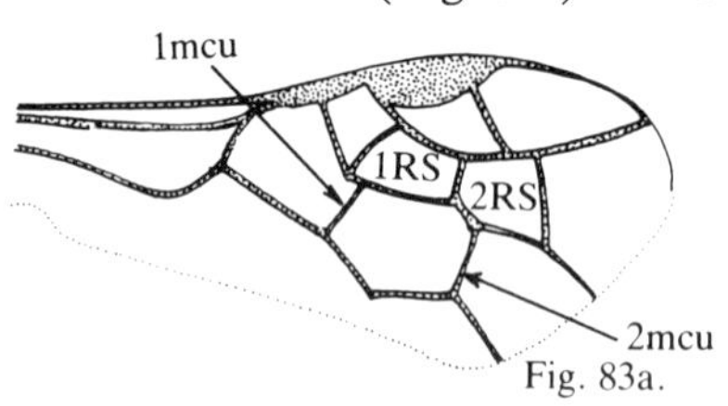

Fig. 83a.

— Veins **1mcu** and **2mcu** of the forewing enter the same cell (Fig. 83b,c), or **2mcu** touches the junction of **1RS** and **2RS** (Fig. 82d,e) 7

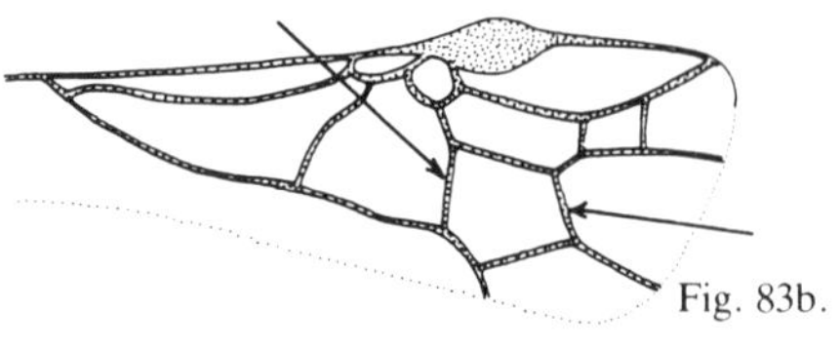
Fig. 83b.

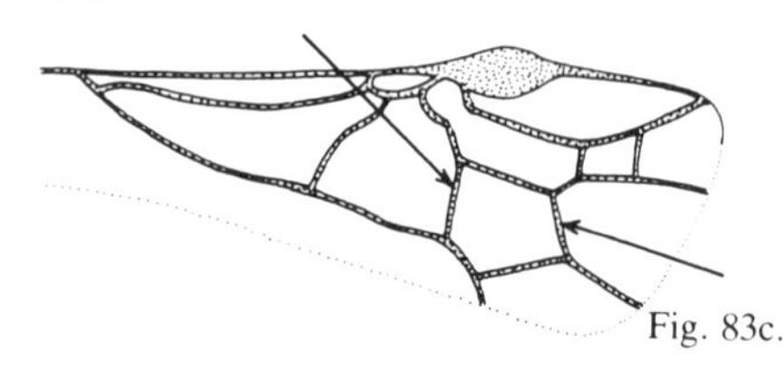
Fig. 83c.

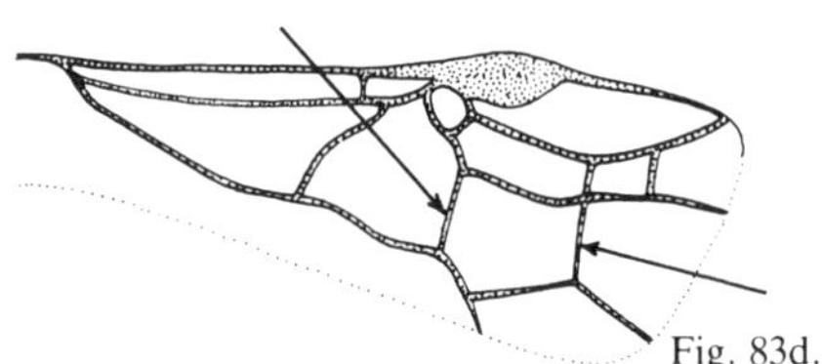
Fig. 83d.

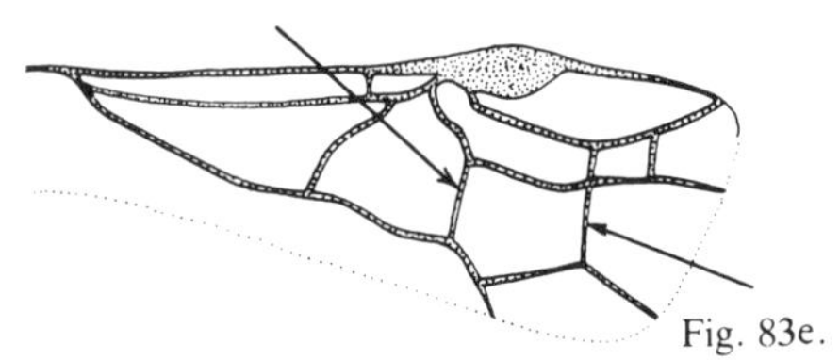
Fig. 83e.

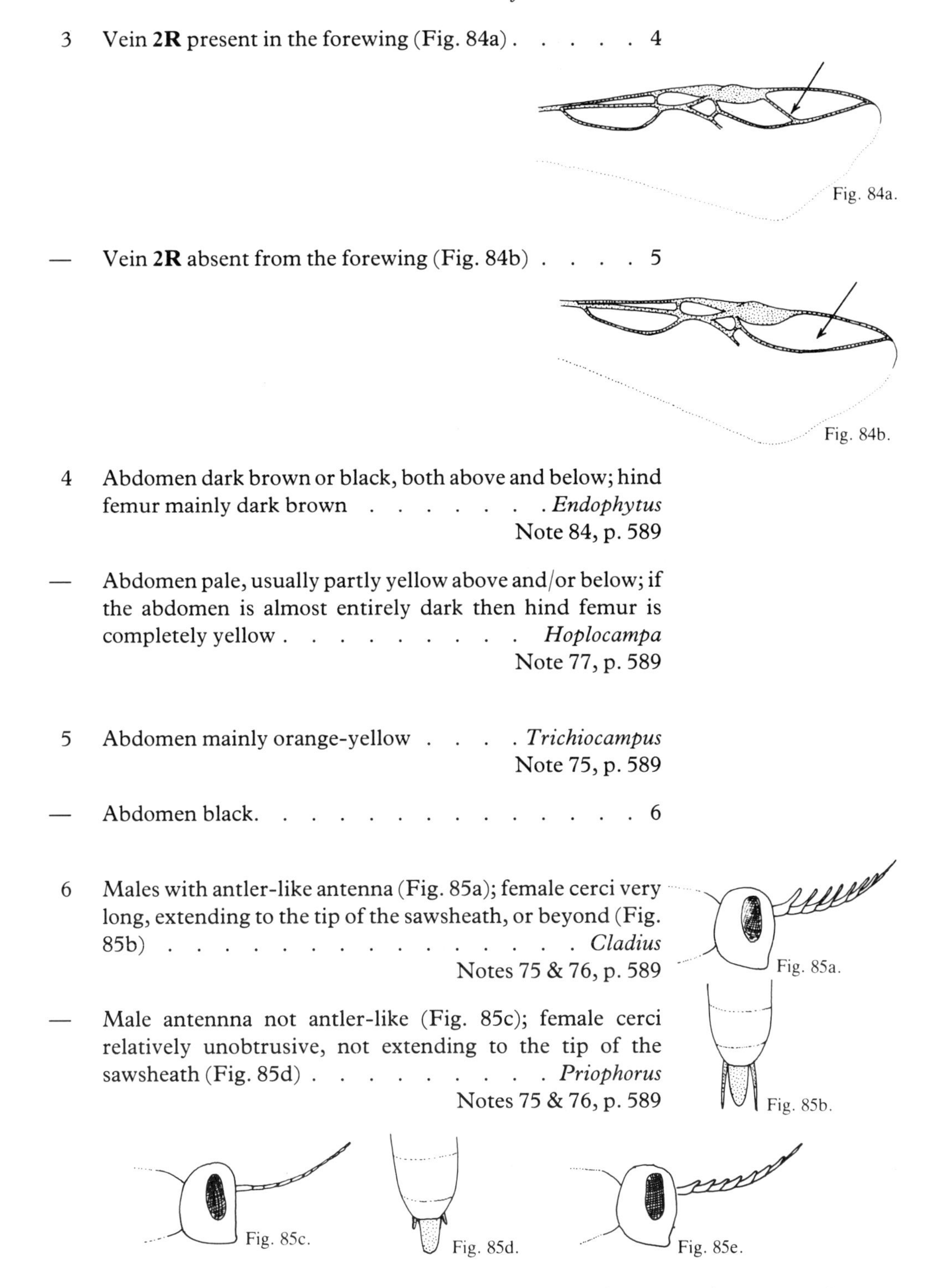

3 Vein **2R** present in the forewing (Fig. 84a) 4

Fig. 84a.

— Vein **2R** absent from the forewing (Fig. 84b) 5

Fig. 84b.

4 Abdomen dark brown or black, both above and below; hind femur mainly dark brown . . . . *Endophytus*
Note 84, p. 589

— Abdomen pale, usually partly yellow above and/or below; if the abdomen is almost entirely dark then hind femur is completely yellow . . . . *Hoplocampa*
Note 77, p. 589

5 Abdomen mainly orange-yellow . . . . *Trichiocampus*
Note 75, p. 589

— Abdomen black. 6

6 Males with antler-like antenna (Fig. 85a); female cerci very long, extending to the tip of the sawsheath, or beyond (Fig. 85b) . . . . *Cladius*
Notes 75 & 76, p. 589

Fig. 85a.

— Male antennna not antler-like (Fig. 85c); female cerci relatively unobtrusive, not extending to the tip of the sawsheath (Fig. 85d) . . . . *Priophorus*
Notes 75 & 76, p. 589

Fig. 85b.

Fig. 85c. Fig. 85d. Fig. 85e.

Note: *P. pilicornis* may have slight apical swellings to the antennal segments, but not antler-like projections (Fig. 85e)

7 Anal cell of the forewing with a basal loop present (Fig. 86a) (If the forewing stigma is white check this character carefully. The colouration of the vein forming this basal loop may also be pale in some species.) 8

— Anal cell of the forewing without an enclosed basal loop (Fig. 86b) 11

8 Vein **2R** present in the forewing (Fig. 87a) 9

— Vein **2R** absent from the forewing (Fig. 87b) 10

9 Anal cell of the hindwing open (Fig. 88a) . . *Endophytus* Note 84, p. 589

— Anal cell of the hindwing closed (Fig. 88b) . . *Hemichroa* Note 78, p. 589

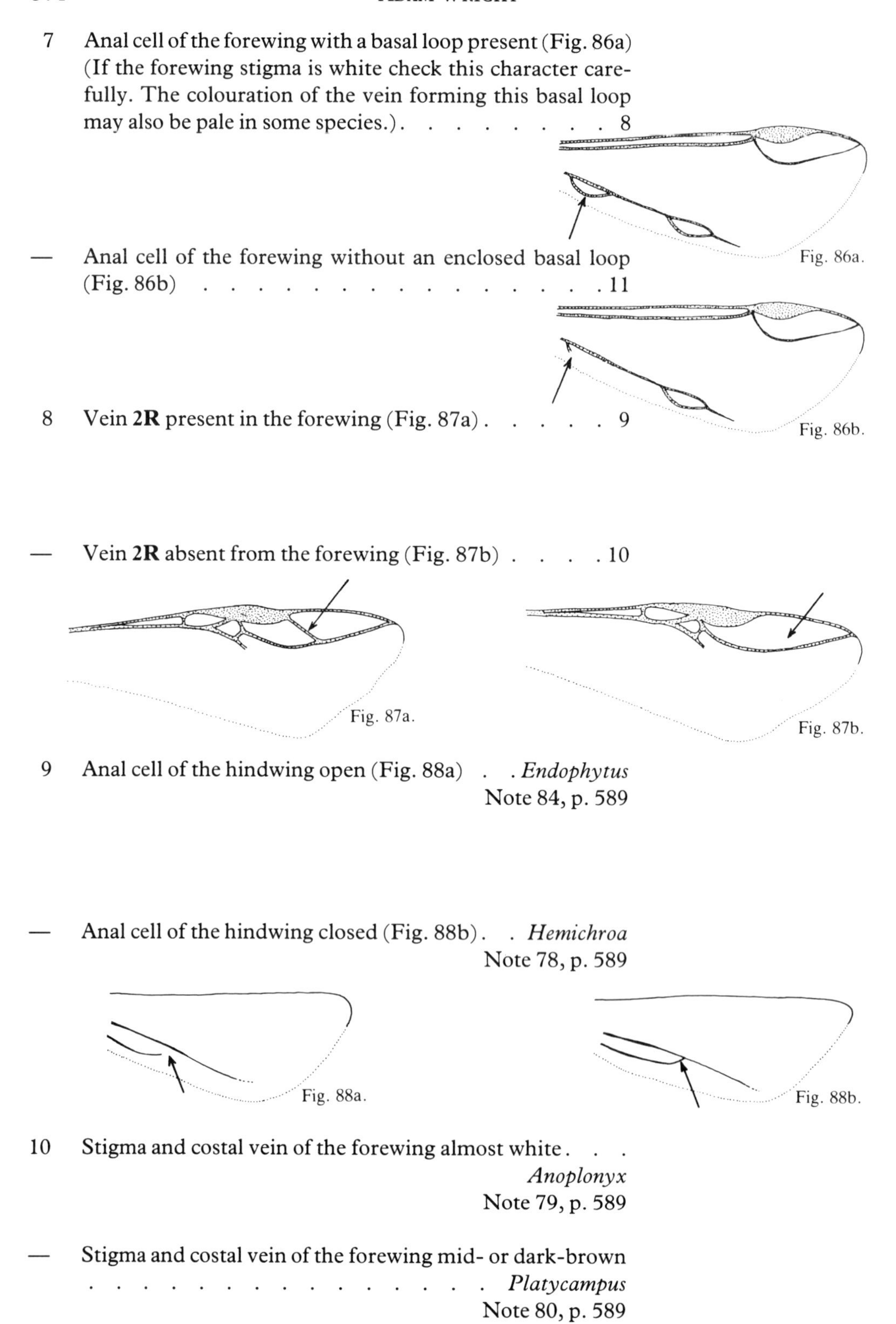

Fig. 86a.

Fig. 86b.

Fig. 87a.

Fig. 87b.

Fig. 88a.

Fig. 88b.

10 Stigma and costal vein of the forewing almost white . . . *Anoplonyx* Note 79, p. 589

— Stigma and costal vein of the forewing mid- or dark-brown . . . . *Platycampus* Note 80, p. 589

11 Vein **Sc** of the forewing touches vein **R** after **M** does (Fig. 89a), or at the same point (Fig. 89b) (view carefully). . . . *Dineura*
Note 81, p. 589

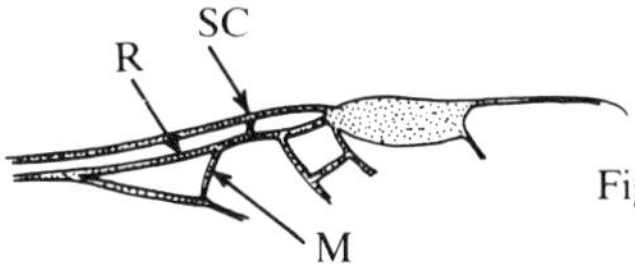

Fig. 89a.

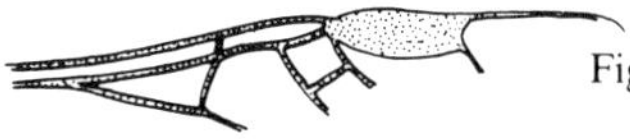

Fig. 89b.

— Vein **Sc** of the forewing reaches vein **R** before **M** does (Fig. 89c) 12

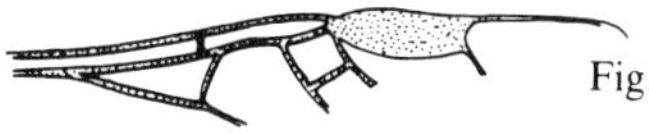

Fig. 89c.

12 Vein **2RM** absent from the forewing (Fig. 90a) 13

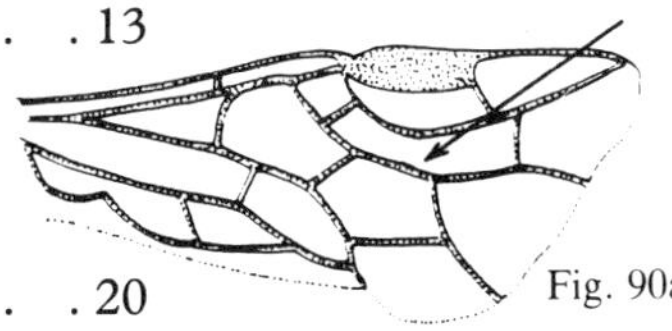

Fig. 90a.

— Vein **2RM** present in the forewing (Fig. 90b,c) 20

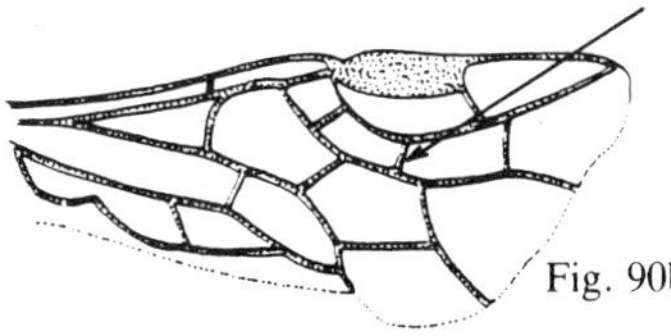

Fig. 90b.

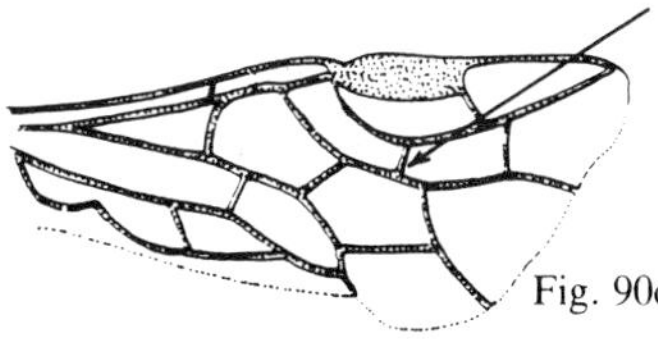

Fig. 90c.

13 Males (apical sternite lacks sawsheath) 14

— Females (sawsheath present) 17

14 Hind edge of the upper surface of the 8th abdominal segment only slightly produced (Fig. 91a) . . . . *Nematinus*
Note 88, p. 590

Fig. 91a.

— Hind edge of the upper surface of the 8th abdominal segment with an apical flange (Fig. 91b). 15

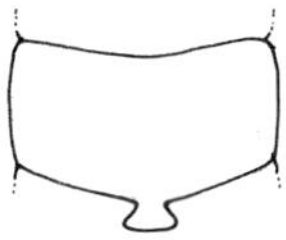

Fig. 91b.

15 Stigma of the forewing all dark, or mainly dark with a pale base . . . . *Euura*
Note 88, p. 590

— Stigma of the forewing extensively pale 16

16 4th tarsal segment produced (extended) below (view from the side) (Fig. 92a). . . . . *Phyllocolpa*
Note 89, p. 590

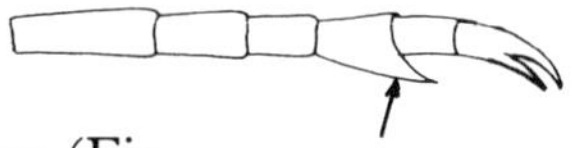

Fig. 92a.

— 4th tarsal segment not produced (extended) below (Fig. 92b) . . . . *Pontania*
Note 89, p. 590

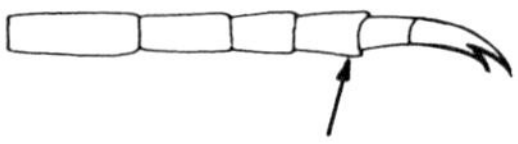

Fig. 92b.

17 Base of the sawsheath almost half as wide as the apex of the abdomen (view from above), or cerci unusually long (extending beyond the tip of the sawsheath) (Fig. 93a,b); size 6–9 mm . . . .
Nematinus
Note 88, p. 590

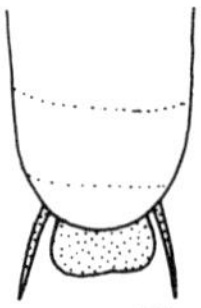

Fig. 93a. 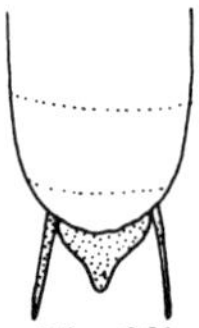 Fig. 93b.

— Sawsheath not as wide, never half as wide as the abdomen (Fig. 93c) OR smaller than 6 mm 18

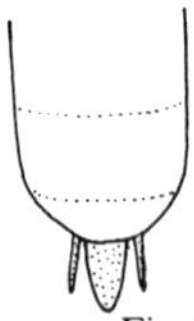

Fig. 93c.

18 Stigma of the forewing all dark, or mainly dark with a pale base; size under 6 mm long . . . . *Euura*
Note 88, p. 590

Note: Females of *Euura* have very long cerci to the sawsheath

— Stigma of the forewing extensively pale (at least half pale); sizes various. 19

19 Apex of the sawsheath smoothly curved (view from the side) (Fig. 94a) . . . .*Pontania*
Note 89, p. 590

— Apex of the sawsheath pointed or unevenly curved (seen from the side) (Fig. 94b,c) . . . . *Phyllocolpa*
Note 89, p. 590

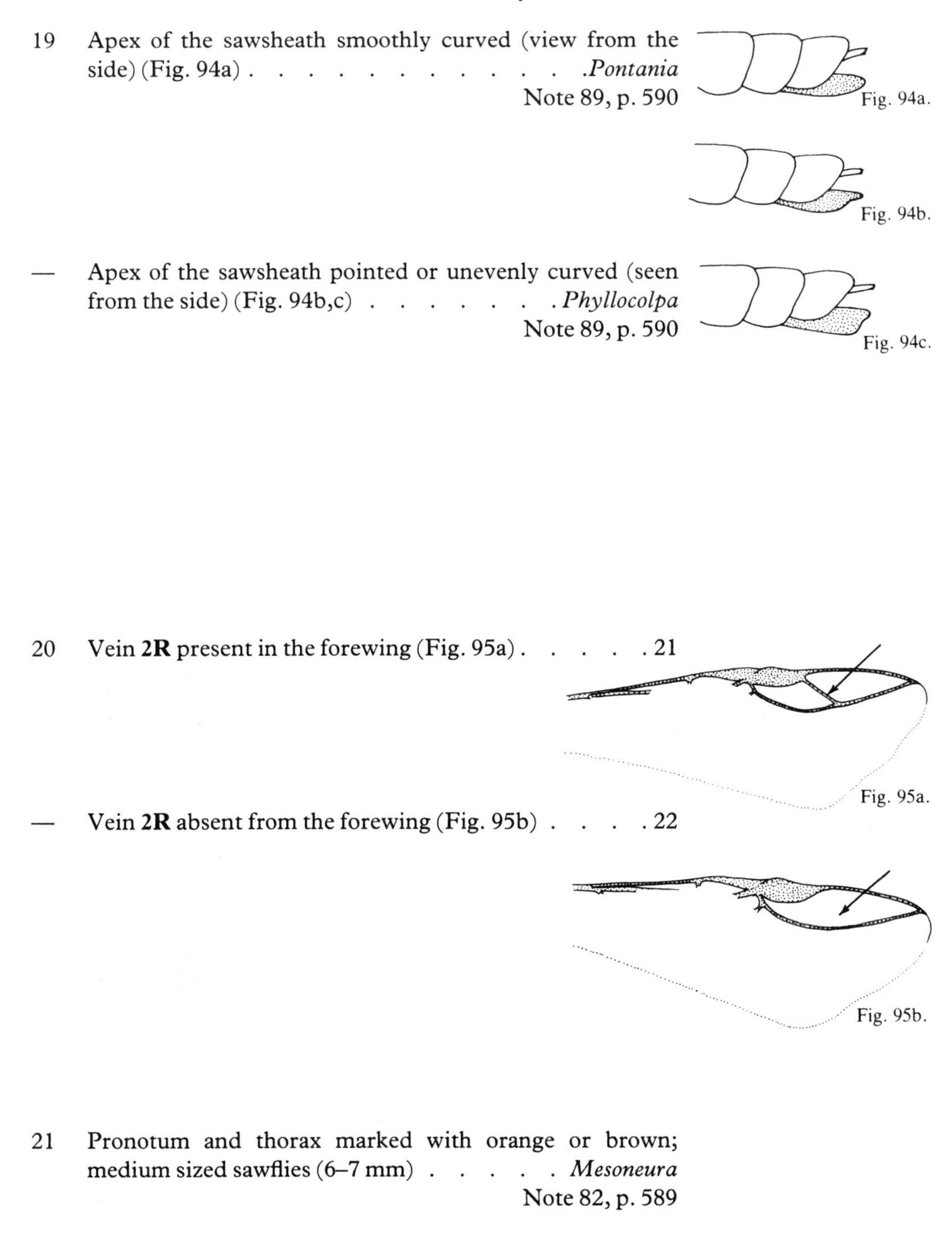

Fig. 94a.

Fig. 94b.

Fig. 94c.

20 Vein **2R** present in the forewing (Fig. 95a) 21

— Vein **2R** absent from the forewing (Fig. 95b) 22

Fig. 95a.

Fig. 95b.

21 Pronotum and thorax marked with orange or brown; medium sized sawflies (6–7 mm) . . . . . . *Mesoneura*
Note 82, p. 589

— Black thorax; small sawflies (less than 5 mm) *Pseudodineura*
Note 83, p. 589

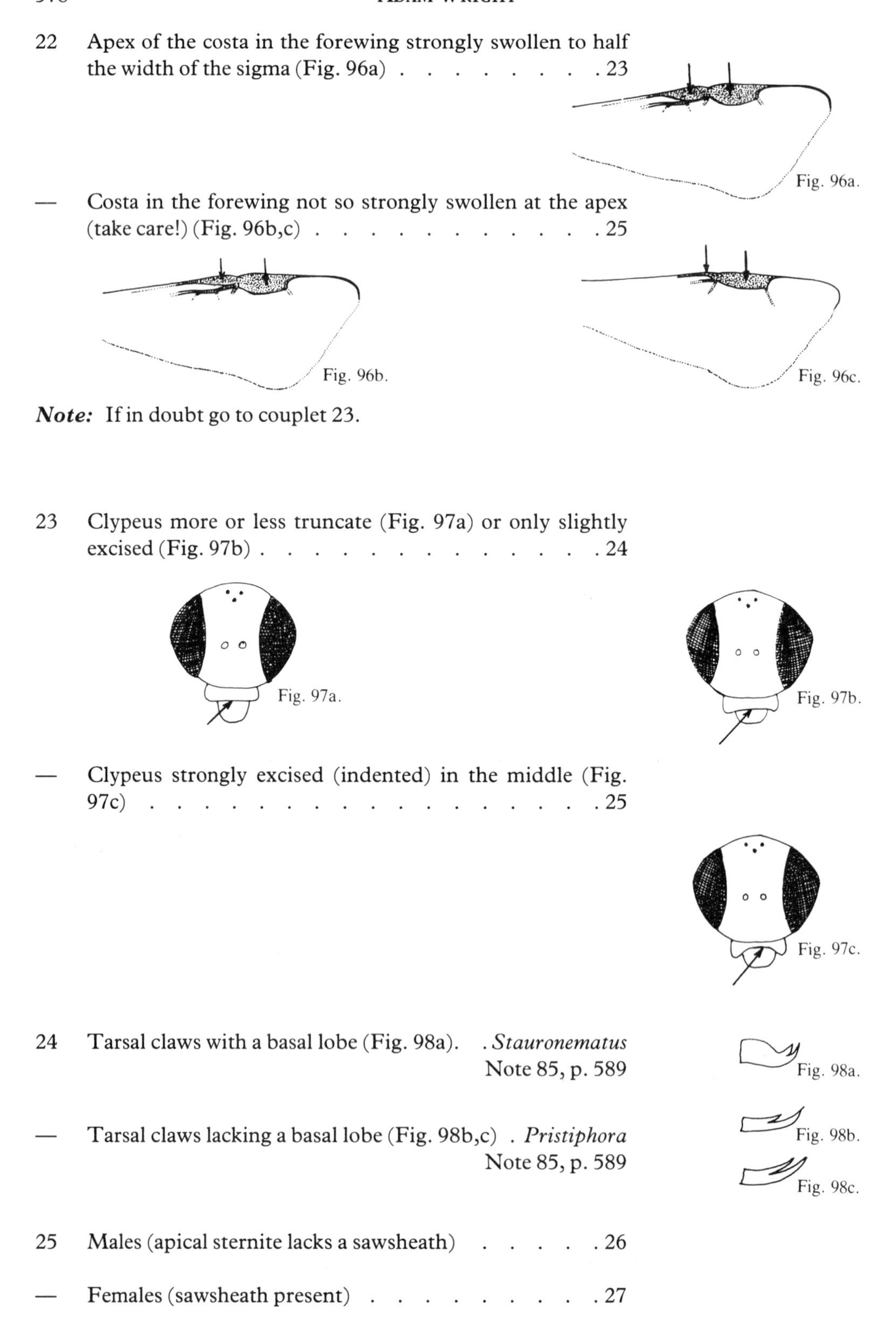

22 Apex of the costa in the forewing strongly swollen to half the width of the sigma (Fig. 96a) 23

Fig. 96a.

— Costa in the forewing not so strongly swollen at the apex (take care!) (Fig. 96b,c) 25

Fig. 96b.

Fig. 96c.

Note: If in doubt go to couplet 23.

23 Clypeus more or less truncate (Fig. 97a) or only slightly excised (Fig. 97b) 24

Fig. 97a.

Fig. 97b.

— Clypeus strongly excised (indented) in the middle (Fig. 97c) 25

Fig. 97c.

24 Tarsal claws with a basal lobe (Fig. 98a). . *Stauronematus* Note 85, p. 589

Fig. 98a.

— Tarsal claws lacking a basal lobe (Fig. 98b,c) . *Pristiphora* Note 85, p. 589

Fig. 98b.

Fig. 98c.

25 Males (apical sternite lacks a sawsheath) 26

— Females (sawsheath present) 27

26 The hind edge of the upper surface of the 8th abdominal segment lacks an apical flange (Fig. 99a) . . *Nematinus*
Note 88, p. 590

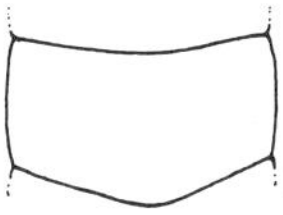

Fig. 99a.

— The hind edge of the upper surface of the 8th abdominal segment has an apical flange (Fig. 99b) 28

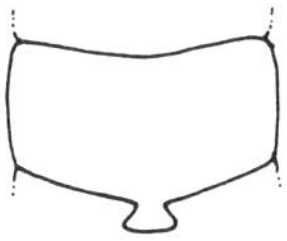

Fig. 99b.

27 Base of the sawsheath almost half as wide as the apex of the abdomen (view from above) (Fig. 100a,b) . . *Nematinus*
Note 88, p. 590

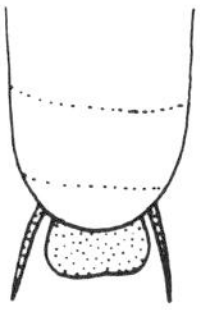

Fig. 100a. 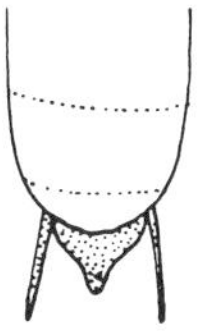 Fig. 100b.

— Base of the sawsheath much narrower than the apex of the abdomen, never nearly half as wide (Fig. 100c) . . . 28

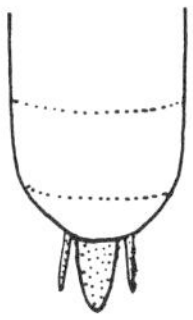

Fig. 100c.

28 Projection between the antennae poorly developed and with a single notch in the middle (Fig. 101a); in side view, the head is scarcely produced between the antennae (Fig. 101b) . . . .
Amauronematus
Note 86 & 87, p. 590

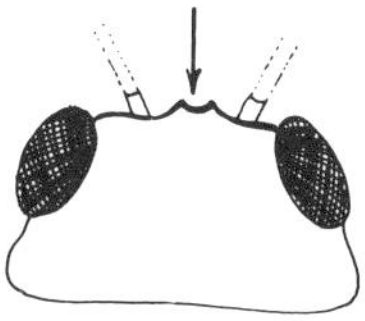

Fig. 101a.

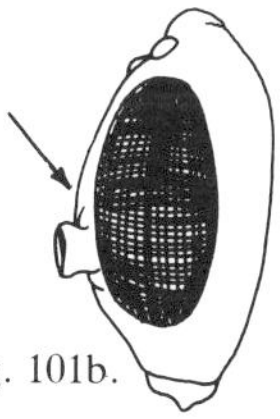

Fig. 101b.

— Projection between the antennae strongly developed (sometimes double notched) (Fig. 101c) OR poorly developed but without a central notch (Fig. 101d); in side view, the head is strongly produced between the antennae (Fig. 101e) 29

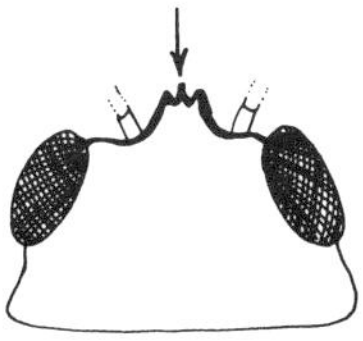

Fig. 101c. 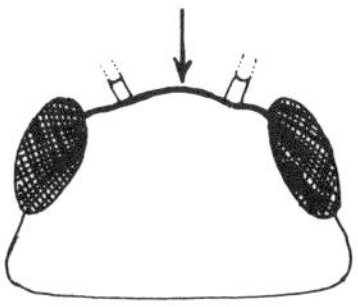 Fig. 101d. 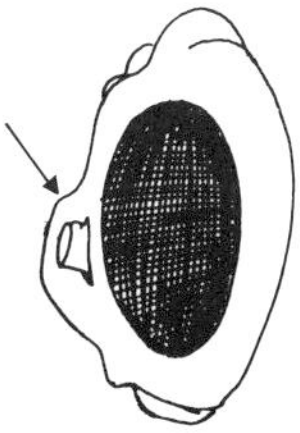 Fig. 101e.

29 Length under 5 mm, with both claws on hind tarsus well developed (Fig. 102a). 30

Fig. 102a.

— Length over 5 mm OR if under 5 mm then the inner claw of the hind tarsus is small (Fig. 102b) 31

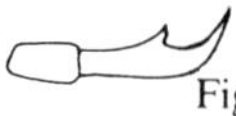

Fig. 102b.

30 4th tarsal segment of the hind leg produced (extended) below (view from the side) (Fig. 103a) . . . . *Phyllocolpa*
Note 89, p. 590

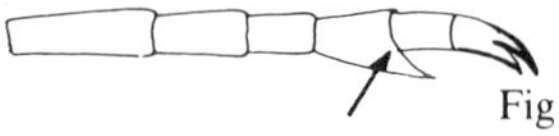

Fig. 103a.

— 4th tarsal segment not produced (extended) below (Fig. 103b) . . . .*Pontania*
Note 89, p. 590

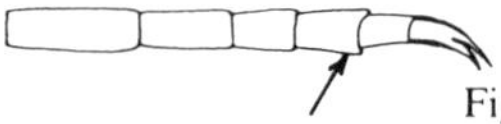

Fig. 103b.

31 Hind tarsal claw with both teeth large (Fig. 104a) *Nematus*
Notes 91 & 92, p. 590

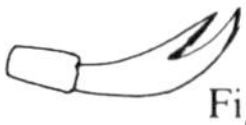

Fig. 104a.

— Hind tarsal claw with the inner tooth small (Fig. 104b). . .
Pachynematus
Note 92, p. 590

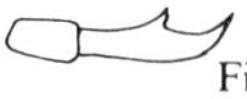

Fig. 104b.

Notes on the British Sawfly Genera

The numbering of the notes corresponds to those given in the keys—to help with cross-referencing.

Xyelidae

1. The distinctive form of the antennae in this family should make identification at this level easy. The xyelids are a small family of sawflies, represented only by the genus *Xyela* in Britain. Two species, *X. julii* Brebisson and *X. longula* Dalman, occur. The former is common and widespread in Britain in early spring (beat scots pine in March–April), but *X. longula* is only known currently from Inverness. Both species are under 5 mm in length, and black with some yellow markings.

Pamphiliidae

Another small family of sawflies, recognised by the many-segmented antennae and central dorsal division of the second abdominal segment. Pamphiliids have large heads and dorso-ventrally (top-to-bottom) flattened abdomens, giving a fairly characteristic appearance. Most species in Britain are large (often 10 mm long), and associated with conifers, or woody angiosperms such as *Populus* or *Rosa*. Four genera occur in Britain.

2. *Acantholyda* is represented by two species which are native to Caledonian pine forests, although *Acantholyda posticalis* Matsumura is now established in conifer plantations even in southern England.
3. *Cephalcia* is represented by a single species, *C. lariciphila* (Wachtl.) which was introduced in the 1950's and is now widespread in British plantations where larch occurs.
4. The genus *Neurotoma* has two British species, both known from Southern and Central England. Neither species is common and *N. mandibularis* (Zaddach) is known only from a handful of sites.
5. *Pamphilius* has fourteen British representatives, which are basically black, or orange-girdled species. All are local and some are extremely scarce. Although most frequently seen basking on leaves, *Pamphilius* spp. are strong flyers and can thus be hard to net!

Megalodontidae

6. Three species, all in the genus *Megalodontes*, were reputedly recorded in Britain. Benson (1943a) states that there is no conclusive evidence to support these claims. Any species keying to this family would obviously require expert checking.

Xiphydriidae

7. Another family represented by only one genus in Britain: *Xiphydria*. They have a very spherical head on a stalked "neck", giving a distinctive appearance. *X. camelus* (L.) is local throughout England, Scotland and Wales, whilst *X. prolongata* (Geoffroy) is largely confined to Southern England. In *X. prolongata* the abdomen is red-girdled, but that of *X. camelus* lacks the red band. These insects are very variable in size, spanning the range 6–21 mm. A third species, *X. longicollis* (Geoffroy), was taken in Windsor Great Park in 1984 (Shaw and Liston, 1987). It is similar in colour to *X. camelus*.

Siricidae

Benson (1943) suggested that two of the eleven species of Siricidae so far recorded from Britain were indigenous to Scottish pine forests but most siricids were originally imported with timber. Six of the recorded species have only been found in imported timber, but the remaining five are now established. Four genera are represented in Britain.

8. The genus *Urocerus* has five species recorded in Britain. The most familiar species is *U. gigas* (L.), the giant wood wasp. The large (up to 40 mm) black and yellow females have the most spectacular ovipositor which is used to bore into conifer bark. Male siricids are much more elusive, normally staying out of reach among the tree canopy. The other four *Urocerus* spp. recorded in Britain are not established here.

9. Four species of *Sirex* have been recorded in Britain, and three are probably now established here. *Sirex* females are blue-black in colour, but males have a predominantly orange abdomen. They range from 15–30 mm in length.

10. *Xeris spectrum* (L.) is the only British representative of this genus. Its distinctive thoracic stripes ease identification. This species, which measures 15–30 mm, has only recently shown signs of becoming established in Britain.

11. *Tremex columba* (L.) has so far only been found in imported timber.

Orussidae

12. This family was represented in England by *Orussus abietinus* (Scopoli), a black species with a white flecked, red-girdled abdomen. 9–15 mm long. It was apparently taken on two occasions in the early nineteenth century and is unlikely to be found again.

Cephidae

These long, thin, sawflies (measuring between 4 and 18 mm) are slow flying; adults are often found on flower heads. Cephids lack cenchri and apparently form a link between the sawflies and the more advanced "apocrite" Hymenoptera. Cephid larvae bore within the stems of their host plant, and thus weaken the stalks. Several species feed on cereal crops such as wheat and their presence makes the stems so weak that they break during storms or during harvesting, causing financial losses. Five genera occur in Britain.

13. *Hartigia*, containing three species, can easily be separated since the adults are large (11–18 mm). All *Hartigia* species are scarce, but can sometimes be encountered on hogweed flowers.

14. The two *Janus* species are smaller (6–9 mm), but their larvae, like those of *Hartigia*, attack trees and rosaceous plants. *Janus* spp. are only encountered occasionally.

15. By far the most common cephids are those in the genera *Cephus* and *Calameuta*. Their larvae feed on wild grasses and cereal crops. Most specimens of *Cephus* and *Calameuta* are under 10 mm. Adults are attracted to yellow flowers such as dandelions. *Calameuta* has two British representatives (both common); *Cephus* has three. *Cephus nigrinus* Thomson was first found in Britain in 1932 (Saunt, 1933), and was considered scarce for many years. However, it is now well-established, although not as common as the other two *Cephus* species.

16. There are two *Trachelus* species in Britain which also feed on cereals and grasses. *T. troglodyta* (Fabricius) has not been recorded for over 100 years, but *T. tabidus*

(Fabricius) is found chiefly in south-east England, particularly in fen areas. Records also exist for Glamorgan.

Argidae

Their distinctive 3-segmented antennae make argids easily recognisable. These are robust-looking sawflies, often seen at umbel flowers in hot sunshine. They make little or no attempt to fly away, and are easily caught. Three genera are represented in Britain.

17. *Aprosthema melanura* (Klug) is the only British representative of the genus and only known from a few localities: in the New Forest, Berkshire, Kent and Cambridgeshire.

18. *Sterictiphora* has two British species. *S. furcata* (Villers) is rare, and *S. geminata* (L.) is scarce and local throughout Britain and Ireland. Males of both *Aprosthema* and *Sterictiphora* have a forked 3rd antennal segment, giving them a bizarre but distinctive appearance.

19. Most of the argids encountered will belong to the genus *Arge*, which has twelve British species. These plump insects are usually orange or metallic blue-bodied, and range in size from 5–11 mm. Females have extremely thick lobes to the sawsheath.

Blasticotomidae

20. Represented by the exceedingly rare *Blasticotoma filiceti* Klug, the larvae of which bore in ferns. The adult is 8mm long, and only recorded from a few sites. The only record of it as a native species is from Goldstitch Moss, Staffordshire (Benson, 1951). Other sites are botanical gardens such as Kew, Wisley and Sizergh Castle.

Cimbicidae

21. Cimbicids can be recognised by their antennae which have seven or fewer segments and end in a club. Six genera are reputedly recorded from Britain. Of these, it is doubtful whether genuinely British specimens exist for *Corynis* or *Pseudoclavellaria*.

22. The remaining four genera are all composed of heavily built, large species (10 mm or more). Despite their size, they are rapid flyers in hot weather.

23. The two *Abia* species are attractive metallic-green insects, associated with meadows containing scabious plants. Both are local and scarce.

24. Three species of *Zaraea* occur in Britain, but only *Z. fasciata* (L.) is taken regularly. Its larvae feed on honeysuckle.

25. *Cimbex* and *Trichiosoma* are the largest British cimbicids, attaining lengths of up to 25 mm. The two genera are easily separated by the arching of the first abdominal segment in *Cimbex*, which leaves an exposed pale area. This is absent in *Trichiosoma*. Separation of species within the genera is much more difficult. Considerable confusion still exists over the taxonomic status of some *Trichiosoma* "species". Sadly, the large cimbicids have declined considerably over the last two decades, and even previously common species—such as *T. lucorum* (L.)—are now scarce.

Diprionidae

These stout-bodied sawflies can be recognised by their antennae, which are serrated in females and have unusual feathery projections in males. Their larvae feed on coniferous trees, and several species are pests of coniferous plantations. Five genera occur in Britain.

26. *Monoctenus juniperi* is only found in the Scottish Highlands, Dee Valley and on the island of Rhum, Scotland. Its larvae feed on juniper.
27. *Microdiprion pallipes* (Fallen), at first thought to be restricted to Scottish pine forest relics, was discovered in Central England in 1987 (Wright, 1987).
28. *Neodiprion sertifer* (Geoffroy in Fourcroy) is locally distributed throughout Britain and can sometimes reach pest proportions in pine plantations.
29. Two species of *Diprion* are known in Britain. *D. pini* (L.) is widely distributed; *D. simile* (Hartig) is restricted to Southern England.
30. Four *Gilpinia* species occur in Britain.Two are restricted to Scotland, a third is known only from two Berkshire specimens. The remaining species, *G. hercyniae* (Hartig) is established in spruce plantations across England and Wales.

Tenthredinidae

This is by far the largest sawfly family, worldwide, and the vast majority of British species are tenthredinids (405 out of the 501 sawflies so-far listed for Britain). Seventy-seven genera have British representatives, covering a wide range of ecological niches. It is convenient to subdivide the Tenthredinidae into its sub-families and deal with these in turn.

Selandriinae:

31. Characterised by their strongly recurved RS&M vein. 11 genera. The larvae feed on ferns, grasses, sedges or rushes except for *Nesoselandria morio* (Fabricius) and *Birka cinereipes* (Klug), whose larvae feed on herbaceous plants. *N. morio* is associated with water forget-me-not.
32. *Heptamelus ochroleucus* (Stephens) is the single representative of the genus. A northern species, most common in Scotland. Its larvae are fern stem-borers.
33. *Pseudohemitaxonus sharpi* (Cameron) is only known from a small number of specimens world-wide; five of these are from Northern England and Scotland.
34. *Strombocerus delicatulus* (Fallen) is a very common and distinctively marked green-black insect, found throughout Britain and Ireland. When killed and set, however, the green changes to a pale orange. Associated with ferns, including bracken, and often seen on this plant. There are no other European representatives of this genus.
35. The genus *Strongylogaster* has six British species, although voucher specimens for two cannot be traced. In the two commonest—*S. lineata* (Christ) and *S. xanthoceros* (Stephens)—there is a marked sexual dimorphism. Males have the first and/or second abdominal tergites black, but the rest of the abdomen is orange. In females, the abdomen is deep brown, with a pale-cream apical band to each tergite. *Strongylogaster* larvae attack ferns, and at least four species will feed on bracken. Adults of the commoner species measure about 10 mm.
36. The four British species of *Aneugmenus* are widely distributed, but only the 6 mm long *A. padi* (L.), whose larvae eat bracken, could be considered common.
37. Mention has already been made of the genera *Nesoselandria* and *Birka* (both mono-specific in Britain) (see note 31 above) which Benson (1952) dealt with under the genus *Melisandra*.

38. Two species of *Brachythops* occur in Britain. *B. flavens* (Klug) is encountered quite frequently in damp areas particularly in Northern Britain. The much rarer *B. wustneii* (Konow) is known from a few bogs in Scotland and England.

39. *Selandria serva* (Fabricius) is an extremely common species of wetland areas. 6–8 mm long, with a bright orange-yellow abdomen. *S. sixii* (Vollenhoven) is larger (8–14 mm), with similar coloration, but is much scarcer.

40. The remaining two genera of Selandriinae often require genitalia examination in order to identify down to species level. *Dolerus* and *Loderus* are poor flyers, and are easy to net. They often fold up their legs in the net, thus appearing dead, and will drop out unless care is taken. Both genera lack vein 2RM in the forewing.

41. There are only three British species of *Loderus*, measuring 6–10 mm; only *L. vestigialis* (Klug) is seen frequently. All larvae feed on horsetails.

42. *Dolerus* species, with their shiny black or red-girdled abdomens are similar in appearance to *Loderus* species. Twenty-eight species of *Dolerus* are known to occur in Britain. 7–12 mm long. Larvae feed on grasses, sedges, rushes and horsetails. Several species emerge early in the year.

Heterarthrinae:

43. A small subfamily of about 10 species, all in the genus *Heterarthrus*. Five species occur in Britain. All are small, 5.5 mm at the most. Several species have 10–15 antennal segments, compared with 9 segments in most British tenthredinids. Larvae of *Heterarthrus* are leaf-miners of various trees. The species are not uncommon, but are easily overlooked because of their small size.

Blennocampinae:

This subfamily forms a large part of the British sawfly fauna, being represented by 34 genera (91 species). Their habits vary considerably and are most conveniently dealt with by subdividing them into tribes.

44. Tribe Athaliini. Containing only one genus, *Athalia*, in Britain. *Athalia* are usually 5–7 mm in length, and have black-marked thoraces and orange abdomens and legs. In most species, the tips of the tibiae and tarsal segments are black giving them a banded "football sock" appearance. *A. cordata* Lepeletier is one of the commonest British sawflies, and other species are also abundant particularly in damp areas. *Athalia* species often have 10 or 11 antennal segments. Specific identification can be difficult, and a clear view of the teeth on the female saw may be necessary. Nine species occur in Britain.

45. Tribe Empriini. Six British genera occur. *Harpiphorus lepidus* (Klug) is the sole British representative of its genus. A small (4–5 mm) green and black species, which has only very rarely been found in Britain. It is associated with oak.

46. *Monostegia abdominalis* (Fabricius), the sole representative of this genus, is a black and yellow species measuring up to 8 mm. It is absent from the extreme north of England and Scotland and, in Britain at least, is parthenogenetic.

47. *Monosoma pulverata* (Retzius in Degeer) is also the sole British representative of its genus. It is a black and white species with reddish legs and, like the preceding species, it is parthenogenetic in Britain.

48. Thirteen species of the genus *Empria* have been found in this country. Their distinctive pattern of paired grey spots on black abdominal segments is a character not found in any other British sawflies. Despite the fact that Benson did a considerable amount of work on *Empria*, publishing a major revision in 1938, his 1952 key to species is not easy to use and it is advisable to undertake genitalia preparations for both sexes. *Empria* species usually measure 5–8 mm.

49. The three British *Ametastegia* species are closely related to the four *Protoemphytus* species. All are medium sized (5–8 mm). Between them, they have a wide range of host plants, and several species are frequently encountered.

50. Tribe Allantini. This small tribe contains three European genera, all occurring in Britain. *Taxonus agrorum* (Fallen) has a red-girdled black abdomen; total length 9 mm. Males of *T. agrorum* have a marginal vein running around the hind wing. This species is locally distributed and scarce, becoming rare in Scotland and Ireland.

51. Several of the nine British species of *Allantus* are particularly attractive. The woodland species *A. togatus* Panzer, which is black and yellow, is the only *Allantus* species with a dark wing cloud. A further four species are reasonably common, but the remaining four are all rare.

52. The two British species of *Apethymus* are unusual in that they are on the wing in late summer or autumn, often being seen in September or October. Many sawfly recorders have stopped fieldwork by October and these species may be considerably more common than records indicate. Both are moderate-sized (about 10 mm).

53. Tribe Caliroini. A small tribe of only two genera, represented by five small species (4–6 mm) in Britain. *Endelomyia aethiops* (Fabricius) is a predominantly black species, having a distinctly shaped anal vein in the forewing.

54. There are four *Caliroa* species, whose larvae skeletonise leaves of pear and cherry trees. The commonest species, *C. cerasi* (L.) can reach pest proportions in orchards and is largely parthenogenetic although males are very occasionally found. The adults of all British *Caliroa* are black.

55. Tribe Blennocampini. This tribe contains 14 genera of British sawflies, including 27 species. Most are 5–7 mm long, but the smallest, *Blennocampa pusilla* (Klug) may measure only 3 mm, and the largest *Phymatocera aterrima* (Klug) may reach 9 mm. Both species are black bodied.

56. *Tomostethus nigritus* (Fabricius), *Rhadinoceraea micans* (Klug), *Dicrostema gracilicornis* (Zaddach), *Monophadnus pallescens* (Gmelin) and *Cladardis elongatula* (Klug) are all medium-sized black species, and the sole British representatives of their respective genera.

57. The small (4–5 mm) *Eutomostethus ephippium* (Panzer) occurs in two forms—an all-black predominantly northern form and a mainly southern form with an orange-red thorax. The latter form is very distinctive, enabling easy field identification of this species. Three other British *Eutomostethus* species occur; one of these is confined to Southern England.

58. There are only two known species of *Stethomostus*, both of which occur in Britain. *S. fuliginosus* (Schrank), whose larvae feed on celery-leaved buttercup, is not uncommon, but *S. funereus* (Klug) is very rare.

59. The genus *Periclista* has three native species, of which *P. albida* (Klug) is the most common. *P. lineolata* (Klug) appears to have a disjunct distribution between Southern England and Southern Scotland. *P. pubescens* (Zaddach) is a species of Southern England, although there is a 1987 record for the Midlands (Wright and Lane, 1989).

60. Two species of *Ardis* are found in Britain; both are small (5–6 mm) and predominantly black. *A. brunniventris* (Hartig) occurs throughout most of Britain, but *A. sulcata* (Cameron) is apparently confined to England.

61. *Pareophora pruni* (L.) is another small (5–6 mm) species, which has a predominantly yellow abdomen, although the first and last segments are black-marked. In this respect, it is similar in appearance to the slightly shorter but stouter *Halidamia affinis* (Fallen). Neither species is common, particularly in the North, and *P. pruni* is believed to be absent from Scotland.

62. The remaining six members of the tribe are in the genera *Monophadnoides* and *Claremontia*, which Benson (1952) dealt with as a single genus. The larvae of all six species feed on rosaceous plants and three of the species are quite common. All have black abdomens and measure 5–7 mm.

Tribe Fenusini. Representatives of this tribe are small species (2–5 mm), which spend their larval life as leaf-miners. Seven genera, containing fifteen species, are found in Britain.

63. *Parna tenella* (Klug) shows marked sexual dimorphism. Males have a predominantly yellow abdomen, whilst females are black. *Scolioneura betuleti* (Klug) is black-bodied in both sexes, with reddish-yellow legs.

64. All other British fenusines are drab insects, mainly brown or black in colour. Several species in the genera *Messa, Metallus, Profenusa, Fenusa* and *Fenella* are virtually or entirely parthenogenetic in Britain and males are unknown in six species.

Some fenusines are not uncommon, but they are frequently overlooked and thus it is difficult to give a true idea of their abundance.

Tenthredininae:
This subfamily includes several large sawflies. Ten British genera, containing some 60 species.

65. The sturdy 10 mm *Eriocampa ovata* (L.) was, in Benson's 1952 key, considered a member of the Tribe Blennocampinae, but has now been transferred to the Tenthredininae. It is an entirely black insect except for the chestnut mesonotum of the thorax. This colour combination is only otherwise found in the tiny (4 mm) *Eutomostethus ephippium* (Panzer). *Hemichroa australis* (Lepeletier) and *Mesoneura opaca* (Klug) are superficially similar in colour and size to *E. ovata*, but the former has a chestnut head and *M. opaca* has pale legs. Thus all four species mentioned above are separable, even in the field.

66. *Aglaostigma* has two British representatives, *A. aucupariae* (Klug) and *A. fulvipes* (Scopoli). Both are medium-sized (7–9 mm) black species with a red-girdled abdomen and white markings. *A. fulvipes* is strongly white marked, particularly underneath. Both species are common, most frequently being encountered in damp situations.

67. Five British species of *Tenthredopsis* are recognised at present, but Cameron (1882–1893) had these split into 21 species! Examination of the male genitalia is the only certain way of identifying some individuals. *Tenthredopsis* species are commonly seen, medium to large sized (7–12 mm) and are extremely variable in colour.

68. Two species of *Sciapteryx* may be encountered, although *S. consobrina* (Klug) is very rare and *S. soror* Konow is far from common. Both species are 6–10 mm long, black with white or yellowish markings.

69. *Elinora dominiquei* (Konow) has apparently only been taken once in Britain this century (in Surrey). The scarce 8 mm long *Perineura rubi* (Panzer) shows considerable sexual dimorphism, males having a mainly orange abdomen whilst females have an orange-marked black abdomen.

70. The seven British species of *Rhogogaster* are all green and black in colour and measure between 6–13 mm. The most commonly encountered species, *R. viridis* (L.) and *R. chlorosoma* (Benson) are at the larger end of this size range.

71. There are 27 species of *Tenthredo* currently found in Britain and some, such as those in the *T. arcuata* Forster complex and *T. mesomelas* L., are amongst the most commonly seen of our sawflies. Many species are black and yellow—for example the common *T. celtica* Benson; others are black and red—e.g. *T. livida* L. and *T. ferruginea* Schrank; others are black and green—e.g. the abundant *T. mesomelas*. *Tenthredo* species may often be seen at flower heads or sunbathing on leaves of trees such as silver birch. Most *Tenthredo* sawflies are about 10 mm long, with some reaching 15 mm.

72. Of the 5 *Pachyprotasis* species in Britain, the black and white *P. rapae* (L.) is easily the most common, being found from May–July in large numbers. It is 7–8 mm in length. With the exception of *P. nigronotata* Kriechbaumer (only known from two British examples), *Pachyprotasis* species have the dorsal surface of their abdomens black, although the underside may be green.

73. Several species of *Macrophya* in Britain look superficially like *Tenthredo* species, although the hind legs are considerably longer in *Macrophya* and they have a convex labrum in contrast to the flat one found in *Tenthredo*.

74. Small *Macrophya* in Britain measure about 6 mm, whilst the larger species are 13 mm long. Several species are quite common in Southern England, becoming considerably more scarce in Northern England and in Scotland. The black and red pompilid-mimic *M. annulata* (Geoffroy) is amongst the first species of sawfly one learns to recognise in the field. Eleven species of *Macrophya* are now known in Britain, including the recently discovered *M. parvula* Konow (Liston, 1987) and *M. alboannulata* (Costa) (Liston, 1983a; 1987).

Nematinae:

The rest of the British sawfly fauna belongs to the subfamily Nematinae. Although this comprises only 19 genera, they contain a total of almost 200 British species. Nematine sawflies may be subject to abnormal venation and several are highly variable in colour. In almost all instances genitalia preparations will greatly ease identification at species level and for many species identification is impossible without reference to genitalia.

75. Members of the tribe Cladiini differ from other nematines in that they lack vein 2R and have veins 1MCU and 2MCU entering different cells in their forewings. There are three genera in this tribe. *Trichiocampus*, represented by the single species *T. viminalis* (Fallen) is easily separated by its orange-yellow marked abdomen in contrast to the black of both *Cladius* and *Priophorus*. All species measure between 5 and 9 mm.

76. Male *Cladius* species have antler-like projections to their basal antennal segments, giving a very distinctive appearance. Both British *Cladius* species are common and double-brooded. There are five *Priophorus* species of which *P. pallipes* (Lepeletier) and *P. pilicornis* (Curtis) are the most frequently encountered.

77. The remaining British sawflies are all in the tribe Nematini. The nine British *Hoplocampa* species are usually seen at the blossom of apple, pear, plum, *Sorbus* sp. or hawthorn and their larvae feed on the developing fruit, causing premature falling of fruit and economic losses in orchards. *Hoplocampa* species may be mainly black or, alternatively, mainly yellow. They usually measure between 3 and 7 mm.

78. Both species of *Hemichroa* found in Britain are stoutly built 5–8 mm long insects, and are amongst the most attractive of our sawflies. They are largely parthenogenetic and males are seldom found.

79. *Anoplonyx destructor* Benson has been (accidentally) introduced to Britain. It is a 5–6 mm long black species, with a distinctive white stigma and costal vein in the forewing. The larvae feed on larch, and are considered a pest in plantations.

80. The genus *Platycampus* is monospecific in Britain, being represented by *P. luridiventris* (Fallen), a black and brown species with reddish legs, measuring 5–6 mm. The larvae, which are flat in shape, may be found on the underside of alder leaves.

81. All three known *Dineura* species have been recorded in Britain. As with the last genus, their larvae are flattened and feed on leaves. *Dineura* species may cause identification problems from time to time, because they are particularly prone to wing-venation abnormalities.

82. *Mesoneura opaca* (Klug) is an unremarkable orange-brown marked species, measuring 6–7 mm and associated with oak. It is a common species and entirely parthenogenetic in Britain.

83. Both British species of *Pseudodineura* are usually under 4 mm long. *P. fuscula* (Klug), although not common, is fairly widespread, but *P. enslini* (Hering) is so far believed to be confined (in Britain) to Scotland.

84. *Endophytus anemones* (Hering) was first discovered in Britain in 1957, but the data were lost (Benson, 1961*a*). In 1960, Benson took two larval specimens in Bedfordshire. I have not seen any further published records for the species, whose larvae mine in the leaves of the wood anemone. Adult *E. anemones* are similar in size and appearance to *Pseudodineura*, being small and mainly black.

85. The only British representative of *Stauronematus* is *S. compressicornis* (Fabricius). It is very similar in appearance to some *Pristiphora* species. The genus *Pristiphora* contains about 50 species, which vary in size from small (3–5 mm) species to the 9 mm *P. erichsonii* (Hartig). Several are recent additions to the British fauna (Benson, 1959; Benes and Kristek, 1976; Liston, 1981a, 1981b, 1982, 1983).

86. *Amauronematus* contains about 20 British species. These may be extremely variable in terms of both venation and colouration. They range in size from 4–9 mm.

87. *Amauronematus* species appear early in the year and thus, like *Dolerus*, herald the start of the sawfly season. Most *Amauronematus* species spend their larval stages feeding on willows or sallows. Recent British additions to this genus are noted by Benson (1959) and Lindqvist (1961).

88. There are five species of *Nematinus* in Britain. They are sturdily-built species measuring 6–9 mm. Only two are commonly seen. The five *Euura* species in Britain are all under 6 mm in length. *E. mucronata* (Hartig) is a very common species whose larvae attack willow and sallow buds. Separation of species within the genus *Euura* can be difficult.

89. The genus *Phyllocolpa* was separated from *Pontania* by Benson (1960). In adults, the only constant character that can be used to separate the genera is the shape of the fourth hind tarsal segment. The larvae, however, have completely different habits. Those of *Pontania* feed in leaf galls, whilst *Phyllocolpa* species are leaf-rollers. All members of both genera are confined to *Salix* spp. in Britain.

90. The four British examples of the genus *Croesus* have characteristically enlarged hind tibiae and basal tarsal segments. They are all between 7 and 10 mm long. The most common species, *C. septentrionalis* (L.) has a melanic race in Ireland. Apart from this race, all *Croesus* in Britain have a red-girdled abdomen. Two of the four species are mainly parthenogenetic.

91. There are about 40 British species of *Nematus*. Some are small (about 5 mm) and confined to highland regions of Scotland, but most are larger (up to 11 mm) and many are widespread. Identification to species within *Nematus*, as with most other nematines, is largely dependent upon genitalia features.

92. The last genus, *Pachynematus*, may superficially look similar to *Nematus*. However, males of most species have an extra flap on their penis valve, a feature unique to *Pachynematus* in Britain. About 20 species are so far recorded from Britain, some only recently (Benson, 1961, 1964; Liston, 1980*a*,*b*).

REFERENCES

BENES, K and KRISTEK, J. (1976). A new species of the genus *Pristiphora* (Hymenoptera: Tenthredinidae) feeding on Norway Spruce. *Acta entomologica bohemoslovaka*, **73**, 404–415.

BENSON, R. B. (1943*a*). Some reputed British Sawflies, not found since Stephen's days (Hym: Symphyta). *Entomologist's Monthly Magazine*, **79**, 5–7.

BENSON, R. B. (1943*b*). Studies in Siricidae, especially of Europe and Southern Asia (Hymenoptera: Symphyta). *Bulletin of Entomological Research*, **34**, 27–51.

BENSON, R. B. (1950). An introduction to the natural history of British Sawflies (Hymenoptera: Symphyta). *Transactions of the Society for British Entomology*, **10**, 45–142.

BENSON, R. B. (1951). Hymenoptera 2. Symphyta. Section (a). *Handbooks for the Identification of British Insects*, **6.2(a)**, 1–49.

BENSON, R. B. (1952). Hymenoptera 2. Symphyta. Section (b). *Handbooks for the Identification of British Insects*, **6.2(b)**, 51–137.

BENSON, R. B. (1958). Hymenoptera 2. Symphyta. Section (c). *Handbooks for the Identification of British Insects*, **6.2(c)**, 139–252.

BENSON, R. B. (1959). Sawflies (Hym: Symphyta) of Sutherland and Wester Ross. *Entomologist's Monthly Magazine*, **95**, 101–104.

BENSON, R. B. (1960). A new genus for the leaf-edge-rolling *Pontania* (Hym: Tenthredinidae). *Entomologist's Monthly Magazine*, **96,** 59–60.

BENSON, R. B. (1961*a*). *Endophytus anemones* (Hering), a new British Leaf-mining sawfly (Hym: Tenthredinidae). *Entomologist's Monthly Magazine*, **96,** 171.

BENSON, R. B. (1961*b*). *Pachynematus arcticus* (Lindqvist) comb. Nov., A new British Sawfly in Sutherland (Hym: Tenthredinidae). *Entomologist's Monthly Magazine*, **96,** 137–138.

BENSON, R. B. (1964). *Pachynematus glabriceps* (Lindqvist), A new British Sawfly and a note on *Empria liturata* Gmelin (Hym: Tenthredinidae). *Entomologist's Monthly Magazine*, **100,** 263–264.

CAMERON, P. (1882–1893). *Monograph of the British Phytophagous Hymenoptera*. Vols 1–4. Ray Society, London.

FITTON, M. G., GRAHAM, M. W. R. de V., BOUCEK, Z. R. J., FERGUSSON, N. D. M., HUDDLESTON, T., QUINLAN, J. and RICHARDS, O. W. (1978). A checklist of British Insects. *Handbooks for the Identification of British Insects*, **11(4),** 1–159.

FORESTRY COMMISSION. (1955). *Pine Sawflies*. Forestry Commission leaflet No. 35, 8 pages.

GAULD, I. D. and BOLTON, B. (Eds.). (1988). *The Hymenoptera*. British Museum (Natural History), London, 322 pp.

LINDQVIST, E. (1961). Die Prontopristia Arten Finn lands (Hym. Tenthredinidae). *Notulae entomologicae*, **41,** 69–79.

LISTON, A. D. (1980*a*). Notes on some sawflies (Hym: Symphyta) found in Scotland, with a description of a new species of *Pachynematus* Konow from Wester Ross. *Naturalist, Bradford*, **105,** 51–54.

LISTON, A. D. (1980*b*). Notes on sawflies (Hym: Symphyta) collected in Scotland. *Entomologist's Monthly Magazine*, **115,** 239–245.

LISTON, A. D. (1981*a*). Notes on the little known British *Pristiphora* Lat. (Hym: Tenthredinidae) of the abietina group. *Entomologist's Monthly Magazine*, **117,** 73–75.

LISTON, A. D. (1981*b*). *Pristiphora (Lygaeophora) lanifica* (Zaddach, 1882) new to Britain (Hymenoptera: Tenthredinidae). *Entomologist's Gazette*, **32,** 181–4.

LISTON, A. G. (1982). Some sawflies from Whitlaw Moss Nature Reserve, Southern Scotland, with a species new to Britain (Hym: Symphyta). *Entomologist's Record and Journal of Variation*, **94,** 175–179.

LISTON, A. D. (1983*a*). Distribution and Ecology of the sawflies *Macrophya alboannulata* (Costa) and *M. albicincta* (Schrank) in the West Palearctic. *Faunistische Abhandlungen, Staatliches Museum fur Tierkunde in Dresden*, **10,** 151–153.

LISTON, A. D. (1983*b*). *Pristiphora karvoneni* (Lindqvist) (Hym: Tenthredinidae) new to Britain. *Entomologist's Monthly Magazine*, **119,** 135–136.

LISTON, A. D. (1987). *Macrophya parvula* Konow. (Hymenoptera: Tenthredinidae) new to Britain. *Entomologist's Gazette*, **38,** 125–128.

QUINLAN, J. and GAULD, I. D. (1981). Hymenoptera 2. Symphyta. New edition section (a). *Handbooks for the Identification of British Insects*, **6.2(a),** 1–67.

SAUNT, J. W. (1933). *Cephus nigrinus* Thoms., an addition to the British list of Hymenoptera. *Entomologist's Monthly Magazine*, **69,** 275.

SHAW, M. R. and LISTON, A. D. (1987). *Xiphydria longicollis* (Geoffroy) (Hym: Xiphydriidae) new to Britain. *Entomologist's Gazette*, **36,** 233–235.

STEHR, F. W. (Ed.) (1987). *Immature Insects. XIV* Dubuque, 754 pages

TAEGER, A. (1985). Revision of *Tenthredo. Entomologische Abhandlungen, Staatliches Museum fur Tierkunde in Dresden*, **48,** 83–148.

WRIGHT, A. (1987). *Microdiprion pallipes* (Fallen) (Hymenoptera: Symphyta) in Warwickshire (VC 38): an addition to the English fauna. *Entomologist's Gazette*, **38,** 202.

WRIGHT, A. and LANE, S. A. (1989). Records of sawflies (Hym: Symphyta) new to Warwickshire (VC 38). *Entomologist's Monthly Magazine*, **125,** 127.

FURTHER READING

In addition to those references specifically mentioned in the text, the following articles may prove of interest:

BENSON, R. B. (1931). Notes on the British sawflies of the genus *Athalia* (Hymenoptera: Tenthredinidae) with the description of a new species. *Entomologist's Monthly Magazine*, **67,** 109–114.

BENSON, R. B. (1935). Some new British sawflies, with notes on synonymy etc. (Hymenoptera: Symphyta). *Entomologist's Monthly Magazine*, **71,** 239–245.

BENSON, R. B. (1935). The alien element in the British sawfly fauna. *Annals of Applied Biology*, **22** (4), 754–768.

BENSON, R. B. (1938). A revision of the British sawflies of the genus *Empria* Lepeletier (Hymenoptera: Symphyta). *Transactions of the Society of British Entomology*, **5,** 181–198.

BENSON, R. B. (1941). On the European genera of Fenusini and two unrecognised British species (Hymenoptera: Symphyta). *Proceedings of the Royal Entomological Society of London (b)*, **10,** 85–90.
BENSON, R. B. (1953). Some changes and additions to the list of British sawflies with the description of two new species (Hymenoptera: Tenthredinidae). *Entomologist's Monthly Magazine*, **89,** 150–155.
PERKINS, R. C. L. (1929). Notes on the British species of *Amauronematus* (Tenthredinidae) with special reference to Cameron's determinations and to the occurrence of several species not contained in our lists. *Entomologist's Monthly Magazine*, **65,** 31–33.
SAUNT, J. W. (1924). *Sirex areolatus* Cresson. in Britain. *Entomologist's Monthly Magazine*, **60,** 80.
SAUNT, J. W. (1936). A new British sawfly (Hymenoptera: Symphyta). *Entomologist's Monthly Magazine*, **72,** 118.
WRIGHT, A. (1986). *Sawflies (Hymenoptera: Symphyta) in the collections of the Herbert Art Gallery & Museum, Coventry, UK*. Herbert Art Gallery & Museum, Coventry. 96 Pages

ACKNOWLEDGEMENTS

I would like to thank Ray Barnett and Steve Lane for their constructive criticism of both text and keys. Thanks also to Dave Sheppard for much valued advice and to Liz Hayden-Wells for her diagrams which kept the project alive in the most trying stages. Julia Clarke without your patience and good humour the typing and corrections would have taken for ever—thank you. David John, City Arts and Museums Officer in Coventry also deserves thanks, for without his support I would not have been able to do this work.

Finally, thanks to Andrew Liston, who allowed me to use the list of references to species recently added to the British list which he painstakingly prepared.

APPENDIX

PREPARING SAWFLY GENITALIA FOR EXAMINATION

The successful identification of some sawflies requires examination of their genitalia. In females, it is the characteristic shape of the sawsheath and the teeth of the saws that are important. In males, it is the shape of the penis valves which must be studied. Genitalia should be removed during pinning of the specimen, whilst it is still relaxed. "Old" specimens must be thoroughly re-relaxed prior to genitalia extraction.

Females

The shape of the sawsheath can readily be seen *in situ* by viewing the insect from above and tilting the specimen "head downwards" until a clear view is obtained. However, the saws themselves lie protected within the sawsheath and must be teased out before they can be viewed.

The sawsheath comprises two lobes, between which lie the actual saws. In larger species it is sometimes possible to use a mounted needle or fine forceps to open the sheath and push one or both saws downwards so that they protrude from the sheath. You can then persuade the saw to remain in this position by gently closing the lobes of the sawsheath. Providing at least the first 15 teeth are visible it is usually possible to determine the species involved.

In smaller species (including the nematines) it is advisable to completely remove the saws and mount these separately on celluloid sheet. I stick them to this sheet using dimethyl hydantoin formaldehyde (DMHF) in aqueous solution, but insect mounting gum would suffice. DMHF is available from W.S. Simpson & Co. Ltd., 1–23, Linden Way, Southgate, London N14 4LT. The procedure for removing a saw is as follows. Once again, open the sawsheath, and grasp the saw in a pair of forceps as near to the base of the saw as possible. By pulling and twisting slightly you can then remove the entire saw. This operation is somewhat delicate and if grasped towards its apex the saw may snap, yielding an insufficient length to allow identification. If you pull too hard, you will damage the rest of the specimen. Removal of the saw can be rather a trying occupation, but practice makes the operation easier!

Males

When viewed from above, the abdomen of a male sawfly is open at the end. If you insert a pin into this open pouch, directing the point towards the head of the insect, then by hooking the pin slightly downwards and retracting it the genital armature is normally pulled out of the body. This is much easier to achieve than the removal of female saws, which are necessarily attached by strong muscles.

The genital armature should then be placed on celluloid sheet, in a blob of DMHF solution or mounting gum. Microscopical inspection will show that in the centre of the genital armature are a pair of spines—these are the penis valves. Using pins and fine forceps it is possible to tease out these valves which should be placed away from the rest of the armature. Once the DMHF or glue has dried, the penis valves should be safely contained in this blob, and should be easy to view.

Genitalia preparations are not needed to identify sawflies to genus, but can considerably ease identification to specific level. In some instances, specific identification is not possible without examining genitalia. In the following genera, genitalia preparations will greatly ease identification.

Cimbex (females); *Diprion* (both sexes); *Dolerus* (males); *Loderus* (males); *Empria* (males); *Allantus* (males); *Tenthredopsis* (males); *Rhogogaster* (both sexes); *Tenthredo arcuata complex* (females); and all nematines.

AIDGAP PUBLICATIONS

The following AIDGAP titles have been published by the Field Studies Council:

Insects of the British cow-dung community
P. Skidmore (1991) Occasional Publication 21

British Sawflies (Hymenoptera: Symphyta): a key to adults of the genera occurring in Britain
Adam Wright (1990) Offprint No. 203

Soil Types: a field identification guide
Stephen Trudgill (1989) Offprint No. 196

Keys to the families of British Spiders
L.M. Jones-Walters (1989) Offprint No. 197

A key to adults of British Water Beetles
L.E. Friday (1988) Offprint No. 188

A key to the major groups of British Terrestrial Invertebrates
S.M. Tilling (1987) Offprint No. 187

A key to the major groups of British Freshwater Invertebrates
P.S. Croft (1986) Offprint No. 181

Sea Spiders. A revised key to the adults of littoral Pycnogonida in the British Isles
P.J. King (1986) Offprint No. 179

A field guide to the British Red Seaweeds (Rhodophyta)
Sue Hiscock (1986) Occasional Publication 13

British Grasses: a punched-card key to Grasses in the vegetative state
R.J. Pankhurst & J. Allinson (1985) Occasional Publication 10

Bees, Ants & Wasps – the British Aculeates
Pat Willmer (1985) Occasional Publication 7

A key to the families of British Coleoptera (beetles) and Strepsiptera
D.M. Unwin (1984: revised 1988) Offprint No. 166

A field guide to the Slugs of the British Isles
R.A.D. Cameron, B. Eversham & N. Jackson (1983) Offprint No. 156

A key to the Crabs and Crab-like Animals of British inshore waters
John & Marilyn Crothers (1983: revised 1988) Offprint No. 155

A key to families of British Diptera
D.M. Unwin (1981) Offprint No. 143

An illustrated guide to the Diatoms of British coastal plankton
J.B. Sykes (1981) Offprint No. 140

A field key to the British Brown Seaweeds
Sue Hiscock (1979) Offprint No. 125

These, and many other titles, may be purchased when visiting Field Studies Council Centres or may be ordered through the post from:–

FSC Publications, Field Studies Council, Montford Bridge, Shrewsbury SY4 1HW

or from

Richmond Publishing Co. Ltd., PO Box 963, Slough SL2 3RS.

A complete list of titles and prices is available from either of these addresses.